DISCARD

ANIMAL DRIVES

An Enduring Problem in Psychology

SELECTED READINGS

Edited by
GEORGE A. CICALA
University of Delaware

AN INSIGHT BOOK

D. VAN NOSTRAND COMPANY, INC.

PRINCETON, NEW JERSEY

TORONTO   LONDON

NEW YORK

D. VAN NOSTRAND COMPANY, INC.
120 Alexander St., Princeton, New Jersey
(*Principal Office*)
24 West 40 Street, New York 18, New York

D. Van Nostrand Company, Ltd.
358, Kensington High Street, London, W.14, England

D. Van Nostrand Company (Canada), Ltd.
25 Hollinger Road, Toronto 16, Canada

Published simultaneously in Canada by
D. Van Nostrand Company (Canada), Ltd.

PRINTED IN THE UNITED STATES OF AMERICA

Preface

This book of readings was compiled with the intent of providing in a single volume experiments illustrative of the major problems in animal drives. A glance at the physical dimensions of this book clearly reveals its selective nature. The articles were chosen to illustrate, from both the historical and contemporary viewpoints, fundamental concepts and experimental findings relating to drive research.

Another important consideration in the selection of these particular articles was the relevance of the work for contemporary theories of behavior. The psychologist's interest rests not with physiological processes, nor with the mechanisms responsible for them, but rather with the role played by these processes in determining the behavior of the organism. Indeed, some modern behaviorists maintain that knowledge of the internal conditions of an organism is not necessary for the establishment of psychological principles. They further maintain that the precise specification of antecedent environmental conditions and the careful measurement of subsequent observable behavior are the domain of the psychologist. The view held here is that a thorough understanding of the role of motivation in behavior is not possible without consideration of physiological factors which may alter behavior.

Unfortunately, there is no easy transition from the physiological to the behavioral, that is, from Part I of this book to Part II. However, recent physiological findings have been so compelling, and their relation to psychological concepts of drive so obvious, as to require their consideration in this survey.

The author appreciates the cooperation of the contributing scientists who so kindly permitted their work to be included in this book. He is also grateful to Nancy Dale and Judith K. Corey for their assistance with the many tasks necessary to produce a book of this kind. Jeffrey R. Corey lent valuable assistance in the production of some of the figures. The help of the general editors of the Insight Books series is also appreciated.

GEORGE A. CICALA

Newark, Delaware

Contents

PREFACE   iii

PART I
PHYSIOLOGICAL CORRELATES OF DRIVE

1. AN EXPLANATION OF HUNGER   3
   by W. B. Cannon and A. L. Washburn
2. EXPERIMENTAL HYPOTHALAMIC HYPERPHAGIA IN THE ALBINO RAT   19
   by John R. Brobeck, Jay Tepperman, and C. N. H. Long
3. THE ELICITATION OF A DRINKING MOTOR CONDITIONED REACTION BY ELECTRICAL STIMULATION OF THE HYPOTHALAMIC "DRINKING AREA" IN THE GOAT   50
   by B. Andersson and W. Wyrwicka
4. GLUCOSTATIC MECHANISM OF REGULATION OF FOOD INTAKE   56
   by Jean Mayer
5. POSITIVE REINFORCEMENT PRODUCED BY ELECTRICAL STIMULATION OF SEPTAL AREA AND OTHER REGIONS OF RAT BRAIN   66
   by James Olds and Peter Milner

PART II
THE RELATION BETWEEN DEPRIVATION AND DRIVE

6. ANIMAL BEHAVIOR AND INTERNAL DRIVES   85
   by Curt P. Richter
7. STANDARD APPARATUS FOR THE STUDY OF ANIMAL MOTIVATION   98
   by T. N. Jenkins, L. H. Warner, and C. J. Warden
8. A STUDY OF HUNGER BEHAVIOR IN THE WHITE RAT BY MEANS OF THE OBSTRUCTION METHOD   108
   by L. H. Warner
9. CHANGES IN HUNGER DURING STARVATION   136
   by W. T. Heron and B. F. Skinner

10. DEPRIVATION AND TIME OF TESTING AS DE-
    TERMINANTS OF FOOD INTAKE   148
        by John K. Bare and George A. Cicala
11. RELATION OF RANDOM ACTIVITY TO FOOD
    DEPRIVATION   156
        by Byron A. Campbell and Fred D. Sheffield
12. EATING AND DRINKING AS A FUNCTION OF
    MAINTENANCE SCHEDULE   162
        by William S. Verplanck and John R. Hayes

PART III
THE EFFECTS OF DRIVE ON LEARNING AND PERFORMANCE

13. BEHAVIOR POTENTIALITY AS A JOINT FUNCTION
    OF THE AMOUNT OF TRAINING AND THE DE-
    GREE OF HUNGER AT THE TIME OF EXTINC-
    TION   181
        by C. Theodore Perin
14. TRUE, SHAM, AND ESOPHAGEAL FEEDING AS
    REINFORCEMENTS   208
        by Clark L. Hull, Johnston R. Livingston,
        Richard R. House, and Allen N. Barker
15. REWARD VALUE OF A NON-NUTRITIVE SWEET
    TASTE   222
        by Fred D. Sheffield and Thornton B. Roby
16. REWARD VALUE OF COPULATION WITHOUT
    SEX DRIVE REDUCTION   239
        by Fred D. Sheffield, J. Jepson Wulff, and
        Robert Backer
17. STUDIES OF FEAR AS AN ACQUIRABLE DRIVE:
    I. FEAR AS MOTIVATION AND FEAR-REDUCTION
    AS REINFORCEMENT IN THE LEARNING OF NEW
    RESPONSES   248
        by Neal E. Miller

Part I

Physiological Correlates of Drive

97-193

I

An Explanation of Hunger[1]

W. B. CANNON AND A. L. WASHBURN

[From the Laboratory of Physiology in the Harvard Medical School]

Before the turn of the century, investigators attributed eating, drinking, and sexual behavior to specific but subjectively defined stimuli localized in the organ employed in the consummatory activity. More recently, the central nervous system has been attributed a more important role in producing drive-reducing behaviors. The interested reader is referred to Rosenzweig's excellent historical review of theory and research on hunger and thirst in Psychology in the Making, Leo Postman, ed., Alfred A. Knopf, New York, 1962.

The selection that follows presents evidence for the local stimulus theory of hunger drive. *Although local stimulus theories did not originate with Cannon and Washburn, their statement and the experiments that support it constitute a persistent hypothesis specifying the internal source of hunger, thirst, and sexual stimulation.*

This reading is reprinted from the American Journal of Physiology, 1912, 29, 441-454, *with the permission of the authors and the journal.*

Hunger and appetite are so intimately interrelated that a discussion of either requires each to be clearly defined. According to one view the two experiences differ only

---

[1] The indicative evidence of the results here reported was presented to the Boston Society of Medical Sciences, January 17, 1911. See CANNON: The mechanical factors of digestion, London and New York, 1911, p. 204. The full account was presented to the Harvey Society, New York City, December 16, 1911.

quantitatively, appetite being a mild stage of hunger.[2] Another view, better supported by observations, is that the two experiences are fundamentally different.[3]

Appetite is related to previous sensations of the taste and smell of food; it has therefore, as Pawlow has shown, important psychic elements. It may exist separate from hunger, as, for example, when we eat delectable dainties merely to please the palate. Sensory associations, delightful or disgusting, determine the appetite for any edible substance, and either memory or present stimulation can thus arouse desire or dislike for food.

Hunger, on the other hand, is a dull ache or gnawing sensation referred to the lower mid-chest region and the epigastrium. It is the organism's first strong demand for nutriment, and, not satisfied, is likely to grow into a highly uncomfortable pang, less definitely localized as it becomes more intense. It may exist separate from appetite, as, for example, when hunger forces the taking of food not only distasteful but even nauseating. Besides the dull ache, however, lassitude and drowsiness may appear, or faintness, or headache, or irritability and restlessness such that continuous effort in ordinary affairs becomes increasingly difficult. That these states differ with individuals—headache in one, faintness in another, for example—indicates that they do not constitute the central fact of hunger, but are more or less inconstant accompaniments, for the present negligible. The dull, pressing sensation is the constant characteristic, the central fact, to be examined in detail.

Of the two theories of hunger—(1) that it is a general sensation with a local reference, and (2) that it has a local peripheral source—the former has been more widely accepted. The support for that theory can be shown to be not substantial. The wide acceptance of the theory, however, warrants an examination of it in some detail.

---

[2] Bardier: Richet's Dictionnaire de physiologie, article "Faim," 1904, vi, p. 1; Howell: Text-book of physiology, fourth edition, Philadelphia and London, 1911, p. 285.

[3] See Sternberg: Zentralblatt für Physiologie, 1909, xxii, p. 653. Similar views were expressed by Bayle in a thesis presented to the Faculty of Medicine in Paris in 1816.

HUNGER NOT A GENERAL SENSATION

Underlying the idea that hunger arises from a general condition of the body is the consideration that, as time passes, food substances disappear from the blood, and consequently the nerve cells, suffering from the shortage of provisions, give rise to the sensation.[4]

In support of this view the increase of hunger as time passes has been pointed out. There is abundant evidence, however, that the period of increase is short, and that during continued fasting hunger wholly disappears after the first few days.[5] On the theory that hunger is a manifestation of bodily need, we must suppose that the body is mysteriously not in need after the third day, and that therefore hunger disappears. The absurdity of such a view is obvious.

Continued hunger soon after eating (when the stomach is full), especially in cases of duodenal fistula,[6] and satisfaction when the escaping chyme is restored to the intestine, have been cited as ruling out the peripheral and thus favoring the central origin of the sensation. As will be seen later, however, other possible peripheral sources of hunger exist besides the stomach. Further consideration of this point will be given in due course.

Because animals eat, sometimes eagerly, when the gastro-intestinal tract is wholly separated from the central nervous system,[7] the conclusion has been drawn that hunger must be a general sensation and not of peripheral origin. But appetite as well as hunger may lead to eating. As Ludwig stated many years ago, even if all afferent

[4] Schiff: Physiologie de la digestion, Florence and Turin, 1867, p. 40.

[5] See Luciani: Das Hungern, Hamburg and Leipzig, 1890, p. 113; Tigerstedt: Nagel's Handbuch der Physiologie, Berlin, 1909, i, p. 376; Johansson, Landergren, Sondén, and Tigerstedt: Skandinavisches Archiv für Physiologie, 1897, vii, p. 33; Carrington: Vitality, fasting and nutrition, New York, 1908, p. 555; Viterbi: quoted by Bardier, Loc. cit., p. 7.

[6] See Busch: Archiv für pathologische Anatomie und Physiologie und für klinische Medicin, 1858, xiv, p. 147.

[7] See Schiff: Loc. cit., p. 37; also Ducceschi: Archivio di fisiologia, 1910, viii, p. 582.

nerves were severed, psychic reasons still could be given for the taking of food.[8] Indeed, who accepts dessert because he is hungry? Evidently, since hunger is not required for eating, the fact that an animal eats is no testimony whatever that the animal is hungry, and therefore, after nerves have been severed, is no proof that hunger is of central origin.

Further objections to the theory that hunger is a general sensation lie in the weakness of its main assumption and in its failure to account for certain well-known observations. Thus no evidence exists that the blood has in fact changed when hunger appears. Moreover in fever, when bodily stores are being most rapidly destroyed, and when therefore, according to this theory, hunger should be most insistent, the sensation is wholly absent. And the quick abolition of the pangs soon after food is taken, before digestion and absorption can have proceeded far, as well as the quieting effect of swallowing indigestible stuff, such as moss and clay, further weakens the argument that the sensation arises directly from lack of nutriment in the body.

Many have noted that hunger has a sharp onset. If this abrupt arrival of the characteristic ache corresponds to the general bodily state, the change in general bodily state must occur with like suddenness, or have a critical point at which the sensation is instantly precipitated. No evidence exists that either of these conditions occurs in metabolism.

Another peculiarity of hunger which we have noticed is its intermittency. It may come and go several times in the couse of a few hours. Furthermore, during a given period, the sensation is not uniform in intensity, but is marked by ups and downs, sometimes changing to alternate presence and absence without alteration of rate. Our observations have been confirmed by psychologists, trained to introspection, who have reported that the sensation has a distinctly intermittent course.[9] In the ex-

---

[8] Ludwig: Lehrbuch der Physiologie des Menschen, Leipzig and Heidelberg, 1858, ii, p. 584.

[9] We are indebted to Prof. J. W. Baird of Clark University, and his collaborators, for this corroborative testimony.

perience of one of us (C.) the hunger pangs came and went on one occasion as follows:

Came	Went
12-37-20	12-38-30
40-45	41-10
41-45	42-25
43-20	43-35
44-40	45-55
46-15	46-30

and so on, for ten minutes longer. Again in this relation, the intermittent and periodic character of hunger would require, on the central theory, that the bodily supplies be intermittently and periodically insufficient. During one moment absence of hunger would imply abundance of nutriment in the organism, ten seconds later presence of hunger would imply that the stores had been suddenly reduced, ten seconds later still absence of hunger would imply sudden renewal of plenty. Such zigzag shifts of the general bodily state may not be impossible, but, from all that is known of the course of metabolism, they are highly improbable. The periodicity of hunger, therefore, is further evidence against the theory that the sensation has a general basis in the body.

The last objection to this theory is its failure to account for the most common feature of hunger—the reference of the sensation to the epigastric region. Schiff and others[10] have met this objection by two contentions. First, they have pointed out that hunger is not always referred to the stomach. Schiff interrogated ignorant soldiers regarding the local reference; several indicated the neck or chest, twenty-three the sternum, four were uncertain of any region, and two only designated the stomach. In other words, the stomach region was most rarely mentioned.

The second contention against the importance of local reference is that such evidence is fallacious. Just as the reference of tinglings to fingers which have been removed from the body does not prove that the tinglings originate in those fingers, so the assignment of the ache of hunger

[10] See Schiff: *Loc. cit.*, p. 31; Bardier: *Loc. cit.*, p. 16.

to any special region does not demonstrate that the ache
arises from that region.

Concerning these arguments we may recall first Schiff's
admission that the soldiers he questioned were too few to
give conclusive evidence. Further, the testimony of most
of them that hunger seemed to originate in the region of
the sternum cannot be claimed as unfavorable to a peripheral source of the sensation. The description of feelings which develop from disturbances within the body is
almost always indefinite; the testimony is not, therefore,
dismissed as worthless. On the contrary, such testimony
is used constantly in judging internal disorders.

The force of the contention that reference to the periphery is not proof of the peripheral origin of a sensation
depends on the amount of accessory evidence which is
available. Thus, if an object is seen coming into contact
with a finger, the simultaneous sensation of touch referred to that finger may reasonably be assumed to have
resulted from the contact, and not to have been a purely
central experience accidentally attributed to an outly-
ing member. Similarly in the case of hunger—all that is
needed as support for the peripheral reference of the sensation is proof that conditions occur there, simultaneously
with hunger pangs, which might reasonably be regarded
as giving rise to those pangs. In the fasting stomach may
not conditions, in fact, be present which would sustain
the theory that hunger has a local peripheral source?

Certain assumptions have been made regarding the
state of the fasting stomach, and certain inferences have
been drawn from these assumptions which must be considered before the results we have to present will have a
proper setting.

OBJECTIONS TO SOME THEORIES THAT HUNGER IS OF LOCAL ORIGIN

Hunger is not due to emptiness of the stomach, for
Nicolai found after gastric lavage that the sensation did
not appear in some instances for more than three hours.[11]
This testimony confirms Beaumont's observation on

[11] NICOLAI: Ueber die Entstehung des Hungergefühls, In-
augural-Dissertation, Berlin, 1892, p. 17.

Alexis St. Martin, that hunger arises some time after the stomach is evacuated.[12]

Hunger is not due to hydrochloric acid secreted into the empty stomach. The gastric wash-water from hungry subjects is neutral or only slightly acid.[13] Furthermore, persons suffering from achylia gastrica declare that they have normal feelings of hunger.

Hunger is not due to turgescence of the gastric glands. This theory, propounded by Beaumont,[14] has commended itself to several recent writers. Thus Luciani has accepted it, and by adding the idea that nerves distributed to the mucosa are specially sensitive to deprivation of food, he accounts for the hunger pangs.[15] Also Valenti declared two years ago that the turgescence theory of Beaumont is the only one possessing a semblance of truth.[16] The experimental work reported by these two investigators, however, does not necessarily support the turgescence theory. Luciani severed in fasting dogs the previously exposed and cocainized vagi, and Valenti merely cocainized the nerves; the dogs, eager to eat a few minutes previous to this operation, now ran about as before, but when offered food, licked and smelled it, but did not take it. This total neglect of the food lasted varying periods up to two hours. The vagus nerves seem, indeed, to convey impulses which affect the procedure of eating, but there is no clear evidence that those impulses arise from distention of the gland cells. The turgescence theory would also meet difficulties in an attempt to explain the disappearance of hunger after the swallowing of indigestible material; for such material, not being appetizing, does not cause any secretion of gastric juice.[17] Furthermore, Nicolai found that the sensation could be abolished by simply introducing a stomach tube. The turgescence of the gastric glands would not be reduced by either of these pro-

[12] Beaumont: The physiology of digestion, second edition, Burlington, 1847, p. 51.

[13] Nicolai: Loc. cit., p. 15.

[14] Beaumont: Loc. cit., p. 55.

[15] Luciani: Archivio di fisiologia, 1906, iii, p. 542.

[16] Valenti: Archives italiennes de biologie, 1910, liii, p. 97.

[17] See Pawlow: The work of the digestive glands, London, 1902, p. 70; Hornborg: Skandinavisches Archiv für Physiologie, 1904, xv, p. 248.

cedures. The turgescence theory, finally, does not explain the quick onset of hunger, or its intermittent and periodic character, for the cells cannot be repeatedly swollen and contracted within periods a few seconds in duration.

HUNGER THE RESULT OF CONTRACTIONS

There remain to be considered, as a possible cause of hunger pangs, contractions of the stomach and other parts of the alimentary canal. This suggestion is not new. Sixty-six years ago Weber declared his belief that "strong contraction of the muscle fibres of the wholly empty stomach, whereby its cavity disappears, makes a part of the sensation which we call hunger." [18] Vierordt drew the same inference twenty-five years later (in 1871);[19] and since then Knapp and also Hertz have declared their adherence to this view. These writers have not brought forward any direct evidence for their conclusion, though Hertz has cited Boldireff's observations on fasting dogs as probably accounting for what he terms "the gastric constituent of the sensation." [20]

The argument commonly used against the contraction theory is that the stomach is not energetically active when empty. Thus Schiff stated "the movements of the empty stomach are rare and much less energetic than during digestion." [21] Luciani expressed his disbelief by asserting that gastric movements are much more active during gastric digestion than at other times, and cease almost entirely when the stomach has discharged its contents.[22] And Valenti stated only year before last: "We know very well that gastric movements are exaggerated while digestion is proceeding in the stomach, but when the organ is empty they are more rare and much less pronounced," and therefore they cannot account for hunger.[23]

[18] WEBER: Wagner's Handwörterbuch der Physiologie, 1846, iii², p. 580.
[19] VIERORDT: Grundriss der Physiologie, Tübingen, 1871, p. 433.
[20] KNAPP: American medicine, 1905, x, p. 358; HERTZ: The sensibility of the alimentary canal, London, 1911, p. 37.
[21] SCHIFF: Loc. cit., p. 33.
[22] LUCIANI: Loc. cit., p. 542.
[23] VALENTI: Loc. cit., p. 97.

CONTRACTIONS OF THE ALIMENTARY CANAL IN FASTING ANIMALS

Evidence opposed to these suppositions has been in existence for many years. In 1899 Bettmann called attention to the contracted condition of the stomach after several days' fast.[24] In 1902 Wolff reported that after forty-eight hours without food the stomach of the cat may be so small as to look like a slightly enlarged duodenum.[25] The anatomist His has also observed the phenomenon.[26] Seven years ago Boldireff demonstrated that the whole gastro-intestinal tract has a periodic activity while not digesting.[27] Each period of activity lasts from twenty to thirty minutes, and is characterized in the stomach by rhythmic contractions 10 to 20 in number. These contractions, Boldireff reports, may be stronger than during digestion, and his published records clearly support this statement. The intervals of repose between periodic recurrences of the contractions last from one and a half to two and a half hours. Especially noteworthy is Boldireff's observation that if fasting is continued for two or three days the groups of contractions appear at gradually longer intervals and last for gradually shorter periods, and thereupon the gastric glands begin continuous secretion, and all movements cease. All these testimonies to increased tone and periodic pulsations definitely prove, contrary to previous statements, that the empty stomach may be the seat of vigorous muscular activities.

Boldireff considered hunger in relation to the activities he described, but solely with the idea that hunger might provoke them; and since the activities dwindled in force and frequence as time passed, whereas in his belief they should have become more pronounced, he abandoned the notion of any relation between the phenomena.[28] Did not Boldireff misinterpret his own observations? When he was considering whether hunger might cause the con-

[24] Bettmann: Philadelphia monthly medical journal, 1899, 1, p. 133.

[25] Wolff: Dissertation, Giessen, 1902, p. 9.

[26] His: Archiv für Anatomie, 1903, p. 345.

[27] Boldireff: Archives biologiques de St. Petersburg, 1905, xi, p. 1. See also Ergebnisse der Physiologie, 1911, xi, p. 182.

[28] Boldireff: Loc. cit., p. 96.

tractions, did he not overlook the possibility that the contractions might cause hunger? A number of experiences
have led to the conviction that Boldireff did, indeed,
fail to perceive part of the significance of his results. For
example, in auscultation of the alimentary canal relatively loud borborygmi have been noted as the hunger
pangs were disappearing. Again the sensation can be mo-
mentarily abolished a few seconds after swallowing a
small accumulation of saliva or a tablespoonful of water.
Since the stomach is in high tonus in hunger, this result
can be accounted for as due to the momentary inhibition
of the tonus by swallowing.[29] Thus also could be explained the disappearance of the ache soon after eating
is begun, for repeated swallowing results in continued inhibition.

THE CONCOMITANCE OF CONTRACTIONS AND HUNGER IN MAN

Although the evidence above mentioned had led to
the conviction that hunger results from contractions of
the alimentary canal, direct proof was still lacking. In
order to learn whether such proof might be secured, one
of us (W.) determined to become accustomed to the
presence of a rubber tube in the œsophagus.[30] Almost
every day for several weeks W. introduced as far as the
stomach a small tube, to the lower end of which was
attached a soft-rubber balloon about 8 cm. in diameter.
The tube was thus carried about each time for two or
three hours. After this preliminary experience the introduction of the tube, and its presence in the gullet and
stomach, were not at all disturbing. When a record was
to be taken, the balloon, placed just below the cardia,
was moderately distended with air, and was connected
with a water manometer ending in a cylindrical chamber
3.5 cm. wide. A float recorder resting on the water in
the chamber permitted registering any contractions of
the fundus of the stomach. On the days of observation
W. would abstain from breakfast, or eat sparingly, and

[29] CANNON and LIEB: this Journal, 1911, xxix, p. 267.
[30] NICOLAI (*Loc. cit.*) reported that although the introduction of a stomach tube at first abolished hunger in his subjects,
with repeated use the effects became insignificant.

without taking any luncheon would appear in the laboratory about two o'clock. The recording apparatus was arranged as above described. In order to avoid the possibility of an artifact, a pneumograph, fastened below the ribs, was made to record the movements of the abdominal wall. Between the records of gastric pressure and abdominal movement one electromagnetic signal marked time in minutes, and another traced a line which could be altered by pressing a key. All these recording arrangements were out of W's sight; he sat with one hand at the key, ready, whenever the sensation of hunger was experienced, to make the current which moved the signal.

When W. stated that he was hungry, powerful contractions of the stomach were invariably being registered. The record of W's introspection of his hunger pangs agreed closely with the record of his gastric contractions. Almost invariably, however, <u>the contraction nearly reached its maximum</u> before the record of the sensation was started (see Fig. 1). This fact may be regarded as evidence that the contraction precedes the sensation, and not *vice versa*, as Boldireff considered it. The contractions

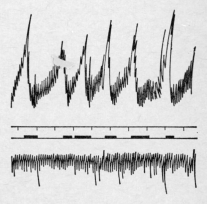

Fig. 1. One half the original size. The top record represents intragastric pressure (the small oscillations due to respiration, the large to contractions of the stomach); the second record is time in minutes (ten minutes); the third record is W's report of hunger pangs; the lowest record is respiration registered by means of a pneumograph about the abdomen.

were about a half-minute in duration, and the intervals between varied from thirty to ninety seconds, with an average of about one minute. W's augmentations of intragastric pressure ranged between 11 and 13 in twenty minutes; C. had previously counted in himself 11 hunger pangs in the same time (see ten-minute record, p. 13). The rate in each of us, therefore, proved to be approximately the same. This rate is slightly slower than that found in dogs by Boldireff; the difference is perhaps correlated with the slower rhythm of gastric peristalsis in man compared with that in the dog.[31]

Before hunger was experienced by W. the recording apparatus revealed no signs of gastric activity. Sometimes a rather tedious period of waiting had to be endured before contractions occurred, and after they began they continued for a while, then ceased (see Fig. 2). The feeling

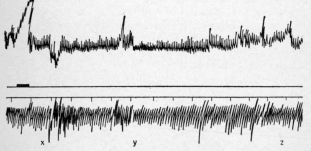

Fig. 2. One half the original size. The same conditions as in Fig. 1 (fifteen minutes). There was a long wait for hunger to disappear. After x, W. reported himself "tired, but not hungry." The record from y to z was the continuance, on a second drum, of x to y.

of hunger, which was reported while the contractions were recurring, disappeared when they stopped. The inability of the subject to control the contractions eliminated the possibility of their being artifacts, perhaps in-

[31] Cannon: The mechanical factors of digestion, London and New York, 1911, p. 54.

duced by suggestion. The close concomitance of the contractions with hunger pangs, therefore, clearly indicates that they are the real source of those pangs.

Boldireff's studies proved that when the empty stomach is manifesting periodic contractions the intestines also are active. Conceivably all parts of the alimentary canal composed of smooth muscle share in these movements. The lower œsophagus in man is provided with smooth muscle. It was possible to determine whether this region in W. was active during hunger.

To the œsophageal tube a thin-rubber finger cot (2 cm. in length) was attached and lowered into the stomach. The little rubber bag was distended with air, and the tube, pinched to keep the bag inflated, was gently withdrawn until resistance was felt. The air was now released from the bag, and the tube further withdrawn about 3 cm. The bag was again distended with air at a manometric pressure of 10 cm. of water. Inspiration now caused the writing lever, which recorded the pressure changes, to rise; and a slightly further withdrawal of the tube changed the rise, on inspiration, to a fall. The former position of the tube, therefore, was above the gastric cavity and below the diaphragm. In this position the bag, attached to a float recorder (with chamber 2.3 cm. in diameter) registered the periodic oscillations shown in Fig. 3. Though individually more prolonged than those of the stomach, these contractions, it will be noted, occur at about the same rate. It is probable that the periodic activity of the two regions is simultaneous, for otherwise the stomach would force its gaseous content into the œsophagus with the rise of intragastric pressure.

What causes the contractions to occur has not been determined. From evidence already given they do not seem to be directly related to bodily need. Habit no doubt plays an important rôle. For present considerations, however, it is enough that they do occur, and that they are abolished when food, which satisfies bodily need, is taken into the stomach. By such indirection are performed some of the most fundamental of the bodily functions.

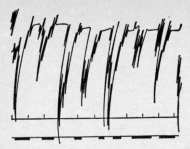

Fig. 3. One half the original size. The top record represents compression of a thin-rubber bag in the lower oesophagus. The pressure in the bag varied between 9 and 13 cm. of water. The cylinder of the recorder was of smaller diameter than that used in the gastric records. The oesophageal contractions compressed the bag so completely that, at the summits of the large oscillations, the respirations were not registered. When the oscillations dropped to the time line, the bag was about half inflated. The middle line registers time in minutes (ten minutes). The bottom record is W's report of hunger pangs.

PECULIARITIES OF HUNGER EXPLAINED
BY CONTRACTIONS

If these contractions are admitted as the cause of hunger, most of the difficulties confronting other explanations are readily obviated. Thus the occurrence of hunger at meal-times is most natural, for, as the regularity of defecation indicates, the alimentary canal has habits. Activity returns at the usual meal-time as the result of custom. By taking food regularly at a definite hour in the evening for several days, a new hunger period can be established. Since at these times the empty stomach, as Boldireff showed, has stronger contractions than the filled organ, hunger is aroused.

The contractions furthermore explain the sudden onset of hunger and its peculiar periodicity—phenomena which no other explanation of hunger can account for. The quick development of the sensation after taking a cold drink is possibly associated with the well-known power of cold to induce contraction in smooth muscle. The great intensity of hunger during the first day of starvation, and its gradual disappearance till it vanishes on the third or fourth day, are made quite clear, for Boldireff observed that gastric contractions in his fasting dogs went through precisely such alterations of intensity and were not seen after the third day.

In fever, when bodily material is being most rapidly used, hunger is absent. Its absence is understood from an observation reported four years ago, that infection with systemic involvement is accompanied by a total cessation of all movements of the alimentary canal.[32] Boldireff observed that when his dogs were fatigued the rhythmic contractions failed to appear. Being "too tired to eat" is thereby given a rational explanation.

Another pathological form of the sensation—the inordinate hunger (bulimia) of certain neurotics—is in accord with the well-known disturbances of the tonic innervation of the alimentary canal in such individuals.

Since the lower end of the œsophagus, as well as the stomach, contracts periodically in hunger, the reference of the sensation to the sternum by the ignorant persons questioned by Schiff was wholly natural. The activity of the lower œsophagus also explains why, after the stomach has been removed, or in some cases when the stomach is distended with food, hunger can still be experienced. Conceivably the intestines also originate vague sensations by their contractions. Indeed the final banishment of the modified hunger sensation in the patient with duodenal fistula, described by Busch, may have been due to the lessened activity of the intestines when chyme was injected into them.

The observations recorded in this paper have, as already noted, numerous points of similarity to Boldireff's observations on the periodic activity of the alimentary canal in fasting dogs. Each period of activity, he found, comprised not only widespread contractions of the digestive canal, but also the pouring out of bile, and of pancreatic and intestinal juices rich in ferments. Gastric juice was not secreted at these times; when it was secreted and reached the intestine, the periodic activity ceased.[33]

[32] Cannon and Murphy: Journal of the American Medical Association, 1907, xlix, p. 840.
[33] Boldireff: Loc. cit., pp. 108-111.

What is the significance of this extensive disturbance? Recently evidence has been presented that gastric peristalsis is dependent on the stretching of gastric muscles when tonically contracted.[34] The evidence that the stomach is in fact strongly contracted in hunger—i.e., in a state of high tone—has been presented above.[35] Thus the very condition which causes hunger and leads to the taking of food is the condition, when the swallowed food stretches the shortened muscles, for immediate starting of gastric peristalsis. In this connection the recent observations of Haudek and Stigler are probably significant. They found that the stomach discharges its contents more rapidly if food is eaten in hunger than if not so eaten.[36] Hunger, in other words, is normally the signal that the stomach is contracted for action; the unpleasantness of hunger leads to eating; eating starts gastric secretion, distends the contracted organ, initiates the movements of gastric digestion, and abolishes the sensation. Meanwhile pancreatic and intestinal juices, as well as bile, have been prepared in the duodenum to receive the oncoming chyme. The periodic activity of the alimentary canal in fasting, therefore, is not solely the source of hunger pangs, but is at the same time an exhibition in the digestive organs of readiness for prompt attack on the food swallowed by the hungry animal.

[34] CANNON: this Journal, 1911, xxix, p. 250.
[35] The "empty" stomach and œsophagus contain gas (see HERTZ: Quarterly journal of medicine, 1910, iii, p. 378; MIKULICZ: Mittheilungen aus dem Grenzgebieten der Medicin und Chirurgie, 1903, xii, p. 596). They would naturally manifest rhythmic contractions on shortening tonically on their content.
[36] HAUDEK and STIGLER: Archiv für die gesammte Physiologie, 1910, cxxxiii, p. 159.

2

Experimental Hypothalamic Hyperphagia in the Albino Rat*

JOHN R. BROBECK, JAY TEPPERMAN,
AND C. N. H. LONG

Although hyperphagia (overeating) due to lesions in the hypothalamic area in the brain had been demonstrated previously (Hetherington and Ranson, American Journal of Physiology, 1942, 136, 609-617), the following selection is presented because of the precision of the techniques employed. Further, it makes the point that the lesions in the ventromedial nuclei of the hypothalamus do not produce metabolic failure as was thought previously. The rats in this study stored fat throughout their bodies, not because fats could not be utilized, but because they ingested more food than they could use. This research strongly suggests that a brain center is in direct control of eating behavior.

The paper is reprinted from the Yale Journal of Biology and Medicine, 1943, 15, 831-853, with the permission of the authors and the journal.

INTRODUCTION

Experimental study of hypothalamic obesity is based upon a foundation laid by clinicians who described lesions of the hypophysio-hypothalamic region in obese human patients. Because of the non-specific character of

* From the Department of Physiological Chemistry, Yale University School of Medicine. The material here presented represents, in part, the data contained in the Thesis of J. R. B. submitted to the Faculty of the School of Medicine in partial fulfillment of the requirements for the degree of Doctor of Medicine. This study was aided by a grant from the John and Mary R. Markle Foundation.

the lesions which they found, previous investigation was naturally directed toward discovering whether damage to the hypothalamus, to the hypophysis, or to both was necessary to produce this condition. A brief review of the data which established the hypothalamic etiology follows.

Hypothalamic obesity was first described by Mohr[42] in a 57-year-old woman who became remarkably obese within the year before her death. At autopsy there was found a hypophysial tumor large enough to deform the sella and to distort and compress the base of the brain, including the cerebral peduncles, optic nerves and chiasma, and the region of the hypothalamus. No attempt was made to explain the excessive deposition of fat nor to distinguish between the hypophysial and the hypothalamic injury.

By the time of publication of Fröhlich's paper[20] in 1901, nine similar reports had already appeared. Fröhlich considered the essential symptoms of the disease to be adiposity and genital underdevelopment caused by pituitary involvement that failed to produce acromegaly. His theory of the hypophysial origin of the condition, although now completely discredited, was supported by the experimental study of Crowe, Cushing, and Homans,[13] Bell,[3] and Dott.[15]

Three years later, Erdheim,[17] in 1904, questioned the validity of Fröhlich's theory, pointing out that in certain cases of this type of obesity the hypophysis had been found to be relatively undamaged, that no particular type of tumor had been found responsible, and that compression of the base of the brain was invariably present when adiposity had been noted. Erdheim therefore concluded that a neural lesion produced the condition, although he was not able to identify the structure concerned. His thesis received experimental substantiation when, in 1912, Aschner[1] observed adiposity in dogs subjected to hypophysial operations which were subsequently found to have injured also the infundibulum. Aschner's results were confirmed by Bailey and Bremer[2] and by Camus and Roussy.[11] The matter was considered to be controversial, however, until Smith[57, 58] reported that no obesity followed lesions restricted to the hypophysis of rats, although obesity appeared in rats with concomitant hypophysial and hypothalamic damage. Grafe and Grün-thal,[23] Biggart and Alexander,[5] and Hetherington and Ranson[26] more recently confirmed Smith's observations. Hetherington,[25] and Hetherington and Ranson,[27] with the aid of the Horsley-Clarke instrument, produced hypothalamic obesity in rats in which, for the first time, direct hypophysial involvement was avoided. Hetherington and Ranson also reported [28] their success in producing typical hypothalamic obesity in hypophysectomized rats. Their study leads to the conclusion that pituitary damage is important in the etiology of obesity only in so far as it may be one cause of hypothalamic pathology, by pressure or by infiltration with tumor.

Although obesity of this type was known clinically for more than a hundred years and was studied rather extensively for 30 years, no attempt appears to have been made to determine the source of the material deposited as fat. Keller and his collaborators observed transient adiposity in dogs and cats with hypothalamic lesions, and found this to be associated with "enhanced appetite" (Keller, Hare, and D'Amour,[32] Keller and Noble,[33, 34] Keller, Noble, and Hamilton[35]). Their published data are inadequate, however, to prove the general thesis that overeating causes hypothalamic obesity.

On the other hand, certain clinicians studying obesity were genuinely interested in the pathogenesis of the condition. Impressed by early quantitative studies of energy metabolism, physicians like Newburgh,[43] Wilder,[64] and others began to emphasize the importance of overeating in producing hypothalamic obesity as well as other types (see also Greene,[24] Bruch,[10] Rony,[52] Evans[18]). Experimental literature, nevertheless, furnished no acceptable confirmation of their clinical hypotheses.

The present study was undertaken to investigate the pathogenesis of hypothalamic obesity in the rat by measuring the energy exchange of animals subjected to hypothalamic operation.

MATERIALS AND METHODS

Obesity was induced in 200-300 gm. albino rats of the Yale or Sprague-Dawley strains, by making bilateral hypothalamic lesions with the aid of the Horsley-Clarke instrument adapted by Clark[12] for use on the rat. Female rats were used for all experiments except the pancreas protein feeding. Under Evipal anesthesia, electrolytic lesions were made with a direct current of 2 milliamperes for 15 seconds, using a unipolar electrode introduced through a drill hole in each parietal bone. The lesions were always placed in approximately the same location, utilizing coordinates which were found to give effective damage. The following control rats were subjected to operation to produce thalamic lesions: 119, 121, 123, 127, 131, 137, 160, 172, and 174.

Each animal with lesions was compared with a control rat of the same strain, age, and initial weight; they were fed identical diets with the exception of control rats 101, 103, 105, and 107 which were changed to a chow diet while the rats with lesions, 100, 102, 104, and 106, were being used for the food choice experiment reported below. Control rats were given more food than they ate daily. The stock diet fed in unmeasured amounts was "dog chow" pellets (Purina). When food intake was to be measured, the rats were given one of the following: (1) finely ground "dog chow" mixed with an equal weight of water; (2) equal parts by weight of water and "calf meal" (Cooperative G. L. F. Mills, Inc., Buffalo, N. Y.); (3) a mixture of ground fresh lean beef, 2000 gm.; corn meal, 2000 gm.; casein, 1000 gm.; lard, 250 gm.; cod-liver oil, 40 gm.; salt mixture, 5 teaspoonfuls; and water, 1750 ml.; (4) a similar mixed diet in which ground fresh pig liver replaced the beef. Diet 3 or diet 4 was prepared by mixing the ingredients, dividing the mass into portions suitable for a day's feeding, freezing the portions and storing them in the freezer; they were later thawed as needed each day. The rats with hypothalamic lesions apparently gained weight more rapidly on the fresh meat diets than on the commercial preparations; in a few instances rats which had almost ceased gaining on "chow" or "calf meal" began to gain again when a fresh meat diet was provided. In other respects, however, uniform results were obtained with the different diets.

Food intake was measured by weighing the individual food cups on a spring balance before and after they were filled daily. One gram per day was arbitrarily allowed for evaporation of water from wet diets, and an attempt was made to control this factor by giving each animal daily only a gram or two more than it was expected to eat. When spilling of food was noted, the rat was given a larger food cup; if this was ineffective in preventing spillage, the amount lost was estimated daily or (as in a few paired feeding experiments) the animal was discarded.

Feeding experiments were also conducted with 2 other diets. In the first of these experiments, Sprague-Dawley male rats were fed a diet containing a protein obtained from beef pancreas (White and Sayers[63]) before and after they were subjected to hypothalamic operation; in the second, 4 female rats with lesions were given the components of diet 3 in separate containers, with olive oil substituted for the lard. Food intake was measured daily.

Paired feeding was carried out on 12 pairs of animals by giving the rat with lesions the amount of food consumed by the control on the previous day. Oxygen consumption and respiratory quotients were estimated during 2- to 3-hour periods when the rats had been deprived of food for from 16 to 24 hours. A modified open circuit Haldane apparatus was used.

Discovery of chronic glomerulonephritis at autopsy of rat 34 led to the examination of urine specimens from a group of obese rats and their controls. Albuminuria was estimated qualitatively by the familiar heat and acetic acid test performed on filtered urine collected under toluol; cells and casts were sought microscopically without centrifugation. Sections for microscopic study of the kidneys were prepared by the Masson technic.

Carcasses and viscera were inspected grossly at the time of death or of sacrifice of the animals. In 10 pairs of rats, blood was drawn from the heart for estimation of blood lipid levels; these analyses were carried out in the laboratory of Dr. E. B. Man by the methods of the following: Man and Gildea,[38] Man and Peters,[40] Man and Gildea,[39] and Bogdanovitch and Man.[6] Endocrine organs were weighed in a series of 12 fat and 9 control rats although the glands have not yet been adequately examined microscopically. Brain-stems were removed before fixation in 4 per cent formaldehyde; they were embedded in paraffin, sectioned serially at 10 micra, and stained by Nissl technic for nuclear identification.

RESULTS

HYPOTHALAMIC HYPERPHAGIA

Hypothalamic lesions which eventually induced adiposity were found to produce an increase in the amount of food eaten by the rat—an increase which was usually evident even before the animal had completely recovered from the operation. As the effects of the Evipal disappeared many of the animals showed locomotor hyperactivity as described by Hetherington and Ranson,[30] but when food was given to these rats they substituted ravenous eating behavior for the locomotion. They voraciously gnawed and ate chow pellets before their pharyngeal reflexes were sufficiently re-established to maintain an adequate airway, and at least 3 rats suffered severe acute (and in one case, fatal) dyspnea from inhalation of food particles. The animal which died had distended its stomach, esophagus, and pharynx with chow. Other animals undoubtedly would have died in a similar way, but from the time of this fatality they were not given free access to food until they appeared to be completely recovered from the anesthetic. Even then they usually ate ravenously, but without untoward complication.

Post-operative behavior of the rats may have been influenced by the Evipal, but the hyperphagia and transient locomotor hyperactivity cannot be attributed to the barbiturate because normal animals and rats with control lesions showed no such behavior during recovery from similar anesthetization.

Because of their voracity the rats increased their body

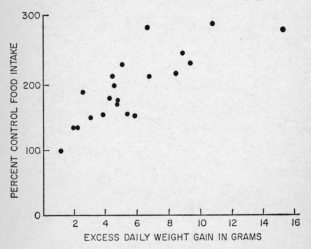

Fig. 1. *Correlation between food intake (as percentage of control intake) and weight gain (in excess of control gain) of obese rats. Each point represents one pair of animals.*

weight by as much as from 20 to 23 grams within the 18 hours following operation. Most of this weight gain undoubtedly represented food in the gut with the water mixed with it. By the end of the first 24-hour post-operative period the hyperphagia was no longer evident on casual inspection, but it was readily proved to be present when the measured food intake of the rats was found to be as much as 3 times the normal daily amount (Table 1). When these rats were relatively restricted by feeding them daily a normal amount of food, they again ate quickly and greedily, consuming in some instances a day's portion in less than an hour.

A definite correlation was found between the rate of weight gain and food intake (Fig. 1). The average daily food intake of each rat with lesions was calculated for

TABLE 1

Body Weight and Rate of Gain

at No.	Weight		Maximal rate of weight gain		
	Initial	Maximal	gm./day	Duration (days)	Food %
11	140				
	258	537	5.0	26	215
C1	126				
	250	289	0.6	26	100
20	215	624	2.7	74	*
33	250	570	6.8	22	*
C4	266	385	0.6	34	*
34	244	850	5.5	26	*
C4	266	424	0.6	34	*
35	261	682	5.3	34	*
C4	266	382	0.6	34	*
36	256	582	6.1	22	*
C4	266	390	0.6	34	*
44	195	500	8.7	9	220
C5	210	310	0.3	9	100
52	218	522	6.6	25	290
C11	226	278	0	25	100

* Food intake unmeasured.

Table 1 (Continued)

| Rat No. | Weight | | Maximal rate of weight gain | | |
	Initial	Maximal	gm./day	Duration (days)	Fo 9
53	237	522	5.8	26	1
C12	237	285	1.1	26	
54	222	670	5.5	25	1
C13	254	393	0.8	25	1
69	225	554	6.6	18	
C68	227				
71	262	572	3.0	16	1
C72	250	371	0	16	1
75	213	526	3.5	28	
C74	222				
90	264	738	6.7	17	2
C93	242	306	0	17	1
94	254	472	2.8	32	1
C95	250	274	0.3	32	1
98	266	472	3.4	28	1
C99	294	352	1.3	28	1
100	285	568	10.1	12	2
C101	272	316	0.8	12	1
102	305	610	11.5	11	2
C103	271	271	0.8	12	1
104	321	583	9.6	12	2
C105	328	344	0.8	12	1
106	291	593	16.0	6	2
C107	259	300	0.8	6	1
118	204	612	5.5	30	1
C119	200	407	1.7	30	1
120	185	458	2.0	51	
C121	188	409†	1.1	51	
122	180	484	4.2	19	1
C123	180	352	3.1	19	1
124	178	385	2.4	37	
C125	182	326	1.2	37	

† C121 was the only rat that became obese following "control" lesions; m scopic sections of the brain-stem are not yet available.

Table 1 (Concluded)

	Weight		Maximal rate of weight gain		
Rat No.	Initial	Maximal	gm./day	Duration (days)	Food %
126	183	396	4.8	8	135
C127	172	322	2.8	8	100
130	195	518	3.9	18	*
C131	195	318	1.5	18	*
136	229	375	2.8	21	*
C137	235	287	1.1	21	*
144	260	466	5.2	12	180
C143	272	334	1.0	12	100
146	256	456	5.2	22	200
C145	250	282	0.7	22	100
159	291	532	5.6	14	233
C160	258	325	0.6	14	100
171	215	285	3.9	10	155
C172	222	227	—1.4	10	100
173	249	440	7.4	14	154
C174	250	296	1.6	14	100

the period of most rapid weight gain, and was compared with the average intake of the control animal (always fed the same diet) during the same period. This comparison is represented in percentage on the ordinate of the graph. The abscissa represents the amount in grams by which the average daily weight gain of the rat with lesions exceeded that of the control rat. The graph shows that the 2 variable quantities are correlated, and the laws of thermodynamics suggest that the relationship is one of cause and effect—that is, food intake determines weight gain.

Data from these experiments are summarized in Table 1, with the number of each rat, the initial and maximal body weights, the maximal rate of weight gain, the length of the period during which this rate was maintained, and the total food intake of that period in percentage of the control intake. ("Maximal weight" or "maximal rate of weight gain" of a control animal is the value observed at the time the obese animal attained its greatest weight or most rapid rate of gain.) The heaviest female rat was number 34, weighing 850 gm. (control weight, 424 gm.), while rat 90 was next heaviest at 738 gm. (control weight, 306 gm.). Other obese rats weighed almost twice as much as their controls. The rate of weight gain was proportionately elevated; rat 106 gained an excess of 15.2 gm./day for a 6-day period, rat 102 outgained its control by 10.7 gm./day for 11 days, and many of the obese rats exceeded the daily average control gain by from 5 to 10 grams for relatively long periods of time. Certain of the rats doubled their own initial weight in 3 months or less (rats 11, 100, and 102); other animals, especially those initially used for paired feeding experiments, gained more slowly but for a longer period of time, attaining their maximal weight only after 10 months or more (rats 34, 54 and 90).

Figure 2 illustrates the course of a typical animal, rat 11, which was the first fat rat studied in these experiments. With respect to food intake and body weight, all similar experiments have confirmed the results of this first experiment. Rat 11 was subjected to 2 operations, the first of which was unsuccessful in that it did not change the level of food intake or rate of weight again. At the second operation a pair of lesions was placed slightly caudal to the first pair. (The coordinates found to be successful at this second operation were used for preparation of most of the other rats of the series.) Food intake was then found to be greatly increased and a rapid weight gain was noted. When restricted to a normal amount of food, the obese animal slowly lost weight, undoubtedly because of its increased oxygen consumption (see below); but hyperphagia again produced weight gain when the rat was later given larger quantities of food.

Figure 3 compares postoperative hyperphagia with preoperative food intake in 2 animals; this figure also illustrates a phenomenon which was further investigated, namely, a tendency for hyperphagia gradually to disappear as the rats became obese. This was not caused simply by recovery from the effects of the lesions, for after 6 obese animals with this tendency had been completely fasted to return their weight to normal, they were again hyperphagic and became obese a second time on re-feeding (Fig. 4). The persistent effect of hypothalamic lesions was also evident in experiments where development of obesity was postponed for several months by the restricted diet of paired feeding experiments (Fig. 7).

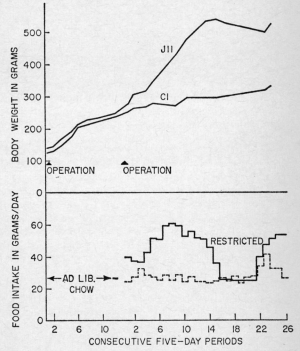

Fig. 2. *Food intake and body weight of rats 11 and C1.*

Male rats maintained on the pancreatic protein-containing diet (White and Sayers[63]) became larger than the female rats of the series, but they also exhibited hyperphagia and obesity following the production of hypothalamic lesions (Fig. 5). One of the pancreatic protein fed male rats with lesions attained a weight of 982 grams, and another now weighs 962 grams, while 3 control animals fed the same diet weigh from 600 to 700 grams. Since the giant rats of Benedict, Horst, and Mendel [4] weighed only 766 and 830 grams, the rats of the present series are apparently the heaviest rats thus far observed.*

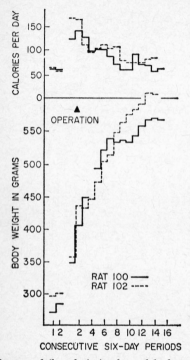

Fig. 3. Average daily caloric intake and body weight of two rats before and after production of hypothalamic lesions.

Paired feeding experiments and determinations of oxygen consumption indicated that in the rats with lesions, total metabolism was not depressed. Under fasting conditions, oxygen consumption was the same in pair-fed rats with lesions and in control rats. With the body

* These rats were cared for by Mrs. Marion Sayers, in the laboratory of Dr. Abraham White.

weight gain of *ad lib.* feeding, the total amount of oxygen utilized by each animal increased significantly, proving that a depressed fasting metabolism was not responsible for the progression of the obesity (Fig. 6). In the

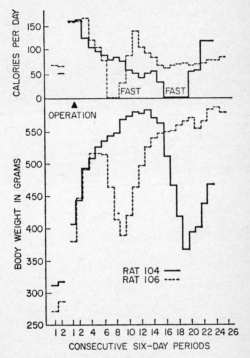

Fig. 4. Effect of prolonged fasting on food intake and body weight of two rats with hypothalamic lesions.

fasting, resting state the obese rats weighing about 600 grams used approximately twice as much oxygen as did the pair-fed rats with lesions or the control rats weighing about 250 grams. The site of utilization of this excess oxygen is not known, but since the abdominal viscera were generally enlarged (see pp. 39-40), their metabolism may have accounted for at least a portion of this oxygen.

On the other hand, animals as large and as heavy as the obese rats would be expected to perform extra muscular work in maintaining posture, respiration, and circulation of the blood.

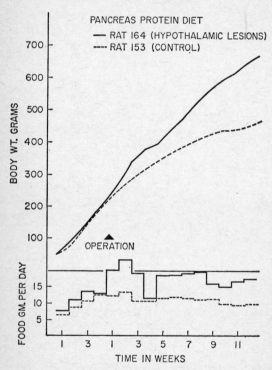

Fig. 5. Hypothalamic hyperphagia in male rat fed a diet containing pancreatic protein.

In 9 out of 12 paired feeding experiments the rat with lesions gained with its control, only to become obese when the former was given larger amounts of food (Fig. 7). Under the conditions of paired feeding the only evident abnormality was habitually rapid eating on the part of the rats with lesions, for they ate a day's portion of food in a relatively few hours. (For discussion of the effects of this type of eating, see Tepperman et al.[61]) In one respect, however, the paired feeding experiments were inconclusive. In 3 pairs of animals the rat with

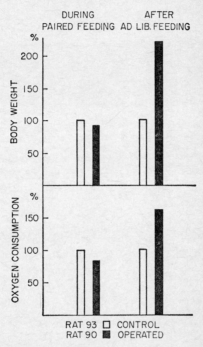

Fig. 6. Fasting resting oxygen consumption of rat 90 before and after the development of obesity.

lesions gained more rapidly than the control when they were fed the same amount of food. The occurrence of this disproportionate gain in greatest degree in the animal which ate a day's portion of food in the shortest time (about one hour) suggests that the phenomenon may be related to the feeding habits of the 3 animals in question. This suggestion is supported by the observations of White and Sayers (personal communication) in paired feeding experiments with unoperated rats. They found that a group of rats fed a pancreatic protein-containing diet ate rapidly and gained more weight than a control group which ate at a slower pace an equivalent amount of a

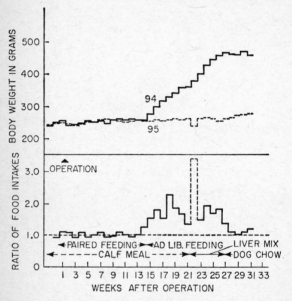

Fig. 7. *Effect of paired feeding on weight gain of rat with hypothalamic lesions. This respone was observed in 9 out of 12 pairs of animals.*

casein-containing diet. Feyder[19] evidently observed a similar disproportionate efficiency of food utilization when he compared the effects of feeding a mixed diet containing sucrose with one containing glucose.

"self selection" of diet

Four rats (100, 102, 104, and 106) were subjected to hypothalamic operation after they and their controls had been maintained for a month in cages where the components of the fresh beef diet were available in separate containers. Since Richter and his associates[47, 48, 50, 51] have found that rats are able to select what are considered to be appropriate dietary elements under a wide variety of experimental conditions, extrapolation of their data

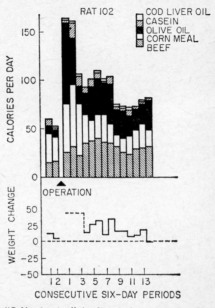

Fig. 8. "Self selection" feeding before and after hypothalamic lesions. Dotted line represents average weight change during 18 days when animal was not weighed.

suggests that if rats with hypothalamic lesions suffered some particular "metabolic" deficit, they would choose some particular component or avoid certain types of food. Diets of the 4 rats, however, showed no consistent change in composition after operation, although all of them ate at least twice as much as before. They were evidently able to become obese on carbohydrate, on protein, or on fat (Figs. 8 and 9). They apparently recognized no inability to utilize fat, for rat 102 spontaneously ingested as much as 14.5 ml. of olive oil daily.

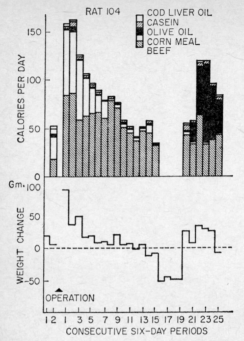

Fig. 9. "Self selection" feeding before and after hypothalamic lesions and after 27-day fast.

KIDNEY FUNCTION

A summary of the albuminuria found in obese rats and in their controls is given in Table 2. The tests were performed on 5 to 9 different days (exceptions: rat 44, one specimen; rat 106, 4 specimens), at periods varying from 4½ to 8 months after operation. In addition to the unquestionable albuminuria of the obese rats, casts were found in profusion and red blood cells were present.

Photomicrographs of sections from the kidneys of rat 34 and its control (Figs. 10 and 11) reveal in the fat rat extensive hyalinization of the glomeruli, with generalized increase in connective tissue and round cell infiltration. The tubules were dilated, their epithelium was thin, and

TABLE 2

Incidence of Albuminuria in Obese Rats
and Controls*

Obese rats			Controls	
52	+ + + +	(Casts)	C 11	SPT
90	+ + + +	(Casts)	C 91	SPT
53	+ + +	(Casts)	C 12	SPT
69	+ +	(Casts)	C 68	SPT
71	+ +	(Casts)	C 72	O
94	+ +	(Casts)	C 95	SPT
54	+		C 13	O
44	+		C 5	O
75	+		C 74	O
106	+		C105	O
98	SPT†		C 99	SPT

* Mean number of observations per rat = 7.
† SPT = slightest perceptible trace.

they contained both formed casts and amorphous material which was probably precipitated protein. Similar changes were found in the kidneys of rat 53, and to a lesser extent in those of rats 54, 69, 71, and 75 (no others

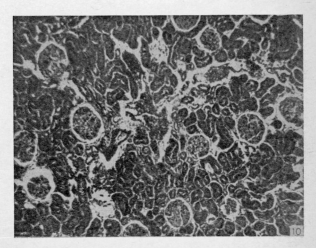

Fig. 10. Photomicrograph of a section from a kidney of control rat C4.

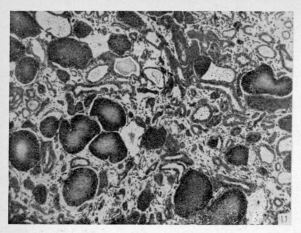

Fig. 11. Photomicrograph of a comparable section from a kidney of obese rat 34.

have been examined). The control rats showed no corresponding involvement.

Abnormalities of kidney function have previously been reported in rats fed diets having a high nucleic acid content (Newburgh and Johnston[44]), and in rats fed diets containing casein rather than liver (Saxton and Kimball[56]). The present series of experiments derives its interest largely from the high incidence of kidney dysfunction in obese human patients (Preble,[45] Dublin and Marks,[16] Evans[18]). With the study of pancreatic diabetes reported by Brobeck et al.,[7] these observations appear to be of some clinical significance, deserving more adequate investigation.

AUTOPSY DATA

Gross examination of the carcasses and viscera of fat rats generally confirmed the work of Hetherington and Ranson.[27, 29] Many of the animals were almost incredibly obese, with an increased amount of fat in every depot of the body—beneath the skin, in the omentum, mesenteries, and retroperitoneal, perirenal, and pericardial tissues. Their gastro-intestinal tracts were found to be both dilated and hypertrophied, weighing (4 pairs of animals) approximately twice as much as those of control rats. This was undoubtedly a result of their hyperphagia, since a similar condition was present in trained normal animals which also ate relatively large amounts of food all at once (Tepperman et al.[61]).

Statistical analysis (Table 3) of the weights of certain

TABLE 3
Autopsy Data

Rat No.	Post-opera-tive day No.	Body weight gm.	Heart gm.	Liver gm.	Kidneys gm.	Adrenals mgm.	Ovaries mgm.
34	444	796	2.05	17.40	5.91	....	46
52	320	426	1.10	13.60	3.25	....	....
53	318	418	1.30	12.00	2.51	44	23
54	318	650	1.60	18.10	2.80	52	32
69	236	569	1.15	18.00	2.60	51	21
71	236	564	1.40	14.55	2.55	64	30
75	236	527	1.10	18.40	2.20	52	35
90	402	598	1.60	25.50	3.53	89	23
94	216	436	1.00	10.00	1.75	49	35
98	216	400	1.15	9.70	2.00	37	25
104	163	464	1.15	14.70	2.20	50	49
106	177	568	1.00	15.30	2.00	60	30
Average		535	1.30	15.60	2.78	55	32
S. E. ±		33.4	0.094	1.250	0.322	4.47	2.56
C4		460	1.34	10.12	2.72	....	84
C11		253	1.20	8.80	1.65	53	85
C13		396	1.10	10.70	2.00	41	46
C72		300	0.90	10.00	2.00	50	108
C93		315	1.00	10.50	2.10	52	75
C95		250	0.80	5.50	1.45	41	49
C99		320	0.85	8.00	1.70	49	36
C105		344	1.00	6.70	1.80	56	58
C107		296	1.00	7.70	1.60	49	50
Average		326	1.02	8.67	1.89	49	66
S. E. ±		22.0	0.057	0.540	0.126	1.90	7.85

organs and endocrine glands showed that the hearts and kidneys of the fat animals were heavier than were those of controls, but the difference was not statistically significant. The ovaries, however, weighed significantly less in obese rats. Although Hetherington and Ranson[27] did not mention the latter change, they described testicular atrophy in the male rats of their series.

Livers of obese animals were almost twice the weight of those of the control rats. The percentage of ether-extractable lipoid in the former was slightly greater than normal when the animals were killed after a 24-hour fast, but when they were killed without previous fasting, the percentage of lipoid was significantly elevated to more than twice the normal level (Table 4). (It should be

TABLE 4

B–OOD AND LIVER LIPIDS

Animal	Total No.	State	Average	S. E. ±	Range
		Blood fatty acids (m. eq.)			
Control	5	fasted	7.7	0.37	6.6–8.7
Obese	5	fasted	11.6	2.36	6.7–20.3
Control	5	fed	9.4	0.74	7.8–12.1
Obese	5	fed	17.9	1.77	14.6–24.4
		Blood cholesterol (mg. p.c.)			
Control	5	fasted	103	2.1	99–108
Obese	5	fasted	119	12.8	85–142
Control	5	fed	106	5.6	90–122
Obese	5	fed	156	9.7	122–176
		Total liver lipids (%)			
Control	3	fasted	9.08	0.331	8.50–9.55
Obese	3	fasted	12.06	1.536	9.73–14.95
Control	3	fed	7.90	0.576	7.17–9.04
Obese	5	fed	19.27	2.185	10.80–23.46

noted that in the normal rats the situation was reversed and the percentage of liver lipoid was greater in the fasting than in the fed state.) Blood lipid levels of the obese rats varied in the same direction; when they were fasted before they were killed, blood cholesterol and fatty acid levels were higher than normal, but the elevation was without statistical significance. In the fed state the elevation from normal was more marked and proved to be statistically significant. Interpretation of these data in terms of specific metabolic processes is not yet possible, but it seems reasonable to suppose that the abnormally high levels in fed obese animals reflected metabolic changes brought about by their unusual eating habits (Tepperman et al.[61]).

Hetherington and Weil [31] found that the weight gain of obese rats was due to storage of fat; true growth with protein synthesis is apparently not accelerated in hypo-thalamic obesity (Long[37]). Measurements of body length in this series showed no deviation from normal, although Hetherington and Ranson[30] previously reported that their rats with lesions were shorter than were control rats. This apparent discrepancy is probably attributable to Hether-ington's having operated on immature, growing animals, while the present series included almost exclusively adult, "plateaued" females in which growth changes would be less likely to appear.

Hypothalamic lesions were fairly uniform from animal to animal, since similar coordinates were used for placing all lesions. Detailed analysis of variations has not been at-tempted. Lesions were usually placed 1 mm. from the midline on each side, and from 0.5 to 1 mm. above the base of the brain (as determined at operation by in-creased resistance to insertion of the electrode) at the level of the anterior border of the median eminence. A

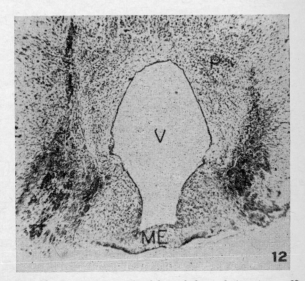

Fig. 12. Photomicrograph of hypothalamic lesions in rat 69. (ME—median eminence; P—paraventricular nucleus; V—third ventricle.)

current of 2 milliamperes for 15 seconds usually produced a cone-shaped block of necrosis with the point of the cone near the fornix and the base of the cone at the base of the brain; this involved the ventromedial portion of the lateral hypothalamic area at that level and the ventro-lateral portion of the central gray substance, including a corresponding portion of the ventromedial nucleus. This nucleus usually was not bilaterally destroyed. Photomicrographs were prepared from sections of the hypothalami of rats 69 and 71 to illustrate the type of lesion just described (Figs. 12 and 13).

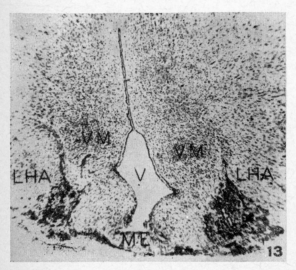

Fig. 13. Photomicrograph of hypothalamic lesions of rat 71. (LHA—lateral hypothalamic area; ME—median eminence; V—third ventricle; VM—ventromedial nucleus.)

Hetherington and Ranson[29] published rather complete descriptions of the hypothalamic lesions of the rats of their study. They were apparently able to interrupt, at various levels through the hypothalamus, paired systems which proceed caudally from their origin in the region of the ventromedial nuclei. Lesions of their animals differed from those of this series in that as a rule the latter were smaller and quite superficial. The neurons involved, or their processes, appeared to be located almost along the inferior surface of the brain-stem at this level. Hetherington (personal communication) has also noted this localization.

DISCUSSION

PATHOGENESIS OF HYPOTHALAMIC OBESITY

Hyperphagia has been previously described following experimental hypothalamic lesions. Keller, Hare, and D'Amour,[32] Keller and Noble,[33, 34] and Keller, Noble, and Hamilton[35] mentioned "enhanced appetite with adiposity" in dogs with hypothalamic lesions. Ranson, Fisher, and Ingram[46] observed "voracious" appetite in a fat monkey with pancreatic diabetes, but they were unwilling to attribute either the adiposity or the diabetes to the diencephalic damage. Following preliminary publication of the results of the experiments in this laboratory (Tepperman, Brobeck and Long[60]), hyperphagia and adiposity were described in rats with hypothalamic lesions (Brooks, personal communication), in monkeys with hypothalamic lesions (Brooks, Lambert, and Bard[8]), and in monkeys with lesions of the posteroventral region of the thalamus and the rostral mesencephalic tegmentum (Ruch, Blum, and Brobeck,[53] and Ruch, Patton, and Brobeck[54]).

The coexistence of hyperphagia and hypothalamic obesity is, therefore, well confirmed. Moreover, the following observations suggest that the adiposity is *caused* by the hyperphagia (rather than by some metabolic disturbance such as an inability to oxidize fat): (1) the rats appeared to be ravenously hungry immediately after operation; (2) when they were freely fed measured amounts of food there proved to be a significant correlation between the degree of hyperphagia and their excess weight gain (Fig. 1); (3) when they were fed *normal* amounts of food they ate quickly and greedily, consuming a 24-hour portion within a few minutes or a few hours; (4) when they were given opportunity to select the composition of their diet, they consistently neither chose nor rejected any particular component, while 2 of the 4 rats ate large amounts of olive oil; (5) during fasting (for as long as 27 days) they were able to use fat as a source of energy in amounts which closely approximated their previous caloric intake (see below). These observations lead almost inescapably to the conclusion that the animals suffered a disturbance which primarily involved the quantitative control of food intake.

This conclusion is supported also by the determinations of oxygen consumption and the paired feeding experiments. In 9 rats with lesions, obesity developed on *ad libitum* feeding after the rate of weight gain had been found to be normal on paired feeding. Estimations of fasting oxygen consumption showed also that when body weights were comparable, oxygen utilization was the same in the operated as in the control rats, but as the animals became obese they used proportionately more oxygen (Fig. 6). A diminished fasting oxygen consumption, therefore, cannot be responsible for the progression of the adiposity. These observations confirm those of Means,[41] who noted a similar phenomenon in human patients. Strang and Evans[59] have pointed out, however, that the significance of observations of this kind frequently has been obscured by expressing oxygen consumption in terms of basal metabolic rate. To evaluate metabolism quantitatively, expression as actual oxygen consumption or with reference to the "ideal" weight of the patient is much to be preferred.

The importance of hyperphagia in the pathogenesis of hypothalamic obesity has been challenged by Hetherington and Ranson,[30] who proposed two alternate theories. In the first of these, they implied that the rats stored fat because they were unable to utilize it as a source of energy. This hypothesis requires a kind of deficit which does not appear to be present either in fat rats or in the fat monkeys of Brooks, Lambert, and Bard;[8] in both series of animals the fat of the adipose tissue disappeared during complete starvation. In the case of the rats, the fat was roughly accounted for on a caloric basis as follows: At the time of initiation of the fast, rat 104 and rat 106 (Fig. 4) were maintaining an almost constant obese weight on a daily intake of from 60 to 75 calories. During the fast they lost weight at a rate of about 8 grams per day, which is equivalent to 72 calories per day if the loss is assumed to have been due solely to oxidation of fat at 9 calories per gram. (Such an assumption is not wholly justified, for they must have been losing also a small amount of protein and some water. At the same time, their total oxygen consumption was probably proportionately decreased.) This rather exact correspondence seems to indicate, however, that oxidation of fat was supplying most of their energy. With the results of the other experiments enumerated above, these observations suggest, contrary to the opinion of Hetherington and Ranson,[30] that the adiposity does not cause, but rather follows, the increased appetite.

Hetherington and Ranson's second theory[30] was based on their observation that rats with lesions ran less than did normal controls when tested for activity in revolvable cages. They attributed adiposity to this relative inactivity rather than to the slight increases in food intake observed in the majority of their rats. Their data suggest that the experiment should be repeated, using rats in which the degree of obesity (and presumably also, hyperphagia) is more pronounced than it was in their series.

Increased food intake has been reported following experimental lesions of other parts of the central nervous system, but with the exception of the thalamo-tegmental lesions reported by Ruch, Patton, and Brobeck,[54] such hyperphagia has not been associated with obesity. The hyperphagia of animals with frontal lobe lesions does not cause excessive weight gain and apparently represents a compensatory adjustment of energy intake to the high level of expenditure associated with the motor hyperactivity which those animals suffer (Fulton, Jacobsen, and Kennard;[22] Richter and Hawkes;[49] Kennard, Spencer, and Fountain;[36] Ruch and Shenkin[55]).

Clinical literature contains a number of references to "morbid appetite" following central nervous system damage (see Fulton,[21] and Watts[62]). Although this increased desire for food has been ascribed to frontal lobe injury, the generalized nature of attendant neurological signs in the absence of adequate postmortem study suggests that hypothalamic dysfunction may have been present in cases of this type.

Hetherington and Ranson[27, 28] have effectively dismissed the previously widely held opinion that this type of obesity in human patients and in experimental animals depends in some way upon hypophysial disturbance. They proved that the adiposity could occur without direct hypophysial involvement, and eventually they produced the condition in completely hypophysectomized rats. The data of the present paper discredit also the supposition that the hypothalamus directly participates in the regulation of the biochemical processes concerned with fat metabolism. Hypothalamic lesions undoubtedly influence the metabolic processes of the animals, but such effects are evidently indirect, and are the result of hypothalamic hyperphagia (Tepperman et al.[61]). Metabolic changes present in animals with hypothalamic lesions have also been found in unoperated rats with abnormal eating habits evoked by training, and certain of these alterations have been observed even in *in vitro* experiments (Dickerson et al.[14]).

Hypothalamic hyperphagia has been observed to cause obesity in the rat, the dog (Keller and others,[32, 33, 34, 35]) and the monkey (Brooks et al.[8]). In these three species, therefore, this type of obesity has been found to be not "endogenous" but "exogenous"—dependent upon the ingestion of more energy-yielding material than the body is able immediately to utilize.

SUMMARY

Investigation of the energy metabolism of experimental hypothalamic obesity in adult albino rats has led to the conclusion that the greatest part of the chemical energy stored as excess fat represents extra food ingested by the animals. The rats appeared to be ravenously hungry almost immediately after operation, eating two or three times the normal amount of food daily when fed *ad libitum*. When they were fed normal quantities of food, they frequently ate a 24-hour portion within a few hours. A significant correlation was established between the extra food intake and excess weight gain.

Metabolic effects of the hypothalamic lesions appeared to be secondary to the hyperphagia. During self-selection feeding experiments and during complete fasting the animals were evidently able to use fat as a source of energy. Their fasting oxygen consumption was the same as that of control rats of comparable weight. On paired feeding, 9 animals with effective lesions gained weight at the same rate as their controls. In 3 other pair-fed rats, however, more rapid gains were observed and the suggestion is made that this phenomenon may have been related to the habitually rapid eating of the rats in question.

Albuminuria was observed in fat rats, with casts and red cells present in the urine. Chronic glomerulonephritis was found on microscopic examination of the kidneys of these animals. Additional changes discovered by post-mortem examination included (besides the obesity): hypertrophy and dilatation of the gastro-intestinal tract, increase in size and weight of the liver, and a decrease in the weight of the ovaries of the obese rats. Blood and liver lipid levels were elevated in obese rats killed without previous fasting.

REFERENCES

1. Aschner, B.: Pflüger's Arch. f. d. ges. Physiol., 1912, 146, 1-146
2. Bailey, P., and Bremer, F.: Arch. Int. Med., 1921, 28, 773-803.
3. Bell, W. B.: Quart. J. Exper. Physiol., 1917, 11, 77-126.
4. Benedict, F. G., Horst, Kathryn, and Mendel, L. B.: J. Nutrition, 1932, 5, 581-97.
5. Biggart, J. H., and Alexander, G. L.: J. Path. & Bact., 1939, 48, 405-25.
6. Bogdanovitch, S. B., and Man, E. B.: Am. J. Physiol., 1938, 122, 73-80.
7. Brobeck, J. R., Tepperman, J., and Long, C. N. H.: Yale J. Biol. & Med., 1943, 15, 893.
8. Brooks, C. McC., Lambert, E. F., and Bard, P.: Fed. Proc., 1942, 1, 11.
9. Bruch, Hilde: Am. J. Dis. Child., 1939, 58, 1282-89.
10. Bruch, Hilde: Am. J. Dis. Child., 1940, 59, 739-81.
11. Camus, J., and Roussy, G.: Rev. neurol., 1922, 38, 622-39.
12. Clark, George: Science, 1939, 90, 92.

13. Crowe, S. J., Cushing, H., and Homans, J.: Bull. Johns Hopkins Hosp., 1910, 21, 127-69.
14. Dickerson, Virginia C., Tepperman, J., and Long, C. N. H.: Yale J. Biol. & Med., 1943, 15, 875.
15. Dott, N. M.: Quart. J. Exper. Physiol., 1923, 13, 241-82.
16. Dublin, L. I., and Marks, H. H.: Proc. Asso. Life Insur. Med. Dir. Am., 1939, 25, 203-32.
17. Erdheim, J.: Sitzungsb. d. k. Akad. d. Wissensch., Wien, 1904, Abt. III, 113, 537-726.
18. Evans, F. A.: Obesity. In: Duncan, G. G., *Diseases of Metabolism*, 1942, Chapt. 10, 513-91.
19. Feyder, S.: J. Nutrition, 1935, 9, 457-68.
20. Fröhlich, A.: Wien. klin. Rundschau, 1901, 15, 883-86; 906-08; reprinted, Res. Publ., Asso. Nerv. & Ment. Dis., 1940, 20, 16-28. See also: Bruch, Hilde: Am. J. Dis. Child., 1939, 58, 1282-89.
21. Fulton, J. F.: J. Michigan Med. Soc., 1934, 33, 175-82.
22. Fulton, J. F., Jacobsen, C. F., and Kennard, Margaret A.: Brain, 1932, 55, 524-36.
23. Grafe, E., and Grünthal, E.: Klin. Wchnschr., 1929, 8, 1013-16.
24. Greene, J. A.: Ann. Int. Med., 1939, 12, 1797-1803.
25. Hetherington, A. W.: Endocrinology, 1940, 26, 264-68.
26. Hetherington, A. W., and Ranson, S. W.: Proc. Soc. Exper. Biol. & Med., 1939, 41, 465-66.
27. Hetherington, A. W., and Ranson, S. W.: Anat. Rec., 1940, 78, 149-72.
28. Hetherington, A. W., and Ranson, S. W.: Endocrinology, 1942, 31, 30-34.
29. Hetherington, A. W., and Ranson, S. W.: J. Comp. Neurol., 1942, 76, 475-99.
30. Hetherington, A. W., and Ranson, S. W.: Am. J. Physiol., 1942, 136, 609-17.
31. Hetherington, A. W., and Weil, A.: Endocrinology, 1940, 26, 723-27.
32. Keller, A. D., Hare, W. K., and D'Amour, M. C.: Proc. Soc. Exper. Biol. & Med., 1933, 30, 772.
33. Keller, A. D., and Noble, W.: Am. J. Physiol., 1935, 113, 79-80.
34. Keller, A. D., and Noble, W.: Am. J. Physiol., 116, 90-91.
35. Keller, A. D., Noble, W., and Hamilton, J. W., Jr.: Am. J. Physiol., 1936, 117, 467-73.
36. Kennard, Margaret A., Spencer, Susan, and Fountain, G.: J. Neurophysiol., 1941, 4, 512-24.
37. Long, C. N. H.: Ann. N. Y. Acad. Sci., 1943, 43, 383-426.
38. Man, E. B., and Gildea, E. F.: J. Biol. Chem., 1932, 99, 43-60.

39. Man, E. B., and Gildea, E. F.: J. Biol. Chem., 1937, 122, 77-88.
40. Man, E. B., and Peters, J. P.: J. Biol. Chem., 1933, 101, 685-95.
41. Means, J. H.: Arch. Int. Med., 1916, 17, 704-10.
42. Mohr: Wchnschr. f. d. ges. Heilk., 1840, 565-71.
43. Newburgh, L. H.: J. Am. Med. Asso., 1931, 97, 1659-63.
44. Newburgh, L. H., and Johnston, Margaret W.: J. Clin. Invest., 1931, 10, 153-60.
45. Preble, W. E.: Boston Med. & Surg. J., 1923, 188, 617-21.
46. Ranson, S. W., Fisher, C., and Ingram, W. R.: Endocrinology, 1938, 23, 175-81.
47. Richter, C. P.: Am. J. Physiol., 1936, 115, 155-61.
48. Richter, C. P., and Eckert, J. F.: Am. J. Physiol., 1936, 116, 128.
49. Richter, C. P., and Hawkes, C. D.: J. Neurol. & Psychiat., 1939, 2, 231-42.
50. Richter, C. P., Holt, L. E., Jr., and Barelare, B.: Am. J. Physiol., 1937, 119, 388-89.
51. Richter, C. P., Holt, L. E., Jr., and Barelare, B.: Am. J. Physiol., 1938, 122, 734-44.
52. Rony, H. R.: *Obesity and Leanness*. Philadelphia, Lea and Febiger, 1940.
53. Ruch, T. C., Blum, M., and Brobeck, J. R.: Am. J. Physiol., 1941, 133, P433-34.
54. Ruch, T. C., Patton, H. D., and Brobeck, J. R.: Fed. Proc., 1942, 1, 76.
55. Ruch, T. C., and Shenkin, H. A.: (In preparation).
56. Saxton, J. A., and Kimball, Grace C.: Arch. Path., 1941, 32, 951-65.
57. Smith, P. E.: J. Am. Med. Asso., 1927, 88, 158-61.
58. Smith, P. E.: Am. J. Anat., 1930, 45, 205-74.
59. Strang, J. M., and Evans, F. A.: J. Clin. Invest., 1928, 6, 277-89.
60. Tepperman, J., Brobeck, J. R., and Long, C. N. H.: Am. J. Physiol., 1941, 133, P468-69.
61. Tepperman, J., Brobeck, J. R., and Long, C. N. H.: Yale J. Biol. & Med., 1943, 15, 855.
62. Watts, J. W.: J. Am. Med. Asso., 1935, 104, 355-57.
63. White, A., and Sayers, Marion A.: Proc. Soc. Exper. Biol. & Med., 1942, 51, 270-71.
64. Wilder, R. M.: Internat. Clin., ser. 42, 1932, 1, 30-41.

The authors wish to express their gratitude for the assistance of Dr. Rolf Katzenstein, Dr. Evelyn Man, Mrs. Marion Sayers, and Dr. Abraham White, as well as for the technical help of Miss Hilda Ritter and Mr. Anthony Rutledge.

3

The Elicitation of a Drinking Motor Conditioned Reaction by Electrical Stimulation of the Hypothalamic "Drinking Area" in the Goat

B. ANDERSSON AND W. WYRWICKA[1]

The following selection indicates hypothalamic control of drinking behavior by showing that, when certain areas of the goat brain are electrically stimulated, the animal responds by drinking. This research also attempts to answer the question concerning the similarity between sensations produced by an electrical stimulus applied to the hypothalamus and sensations produced by thirst due to water deprivation. Andersson and Wyrwicka show that a response, stair climbing, learned when the goat was thirsty and reinforced by permitting the animal to drink, was elicited by direct electrical hypothalamic stimulation. The authors show that the electrical stimulus to the brain will elicit a learned response leading to water, thus indicating the similarity between the electrical brain stimulus and the natural stimuli produced by water deprivation.

This article is reproduced from the Acta Physiologica Scandinavica, *1957, 41, 194-198, with the permission of the authors and the journal.*

It has been shown that osmotic (ANDERSSON 1952, 1953) and electrical stimulation (ANDERSSON and Mc-CANN 1955 a, b, GREER 1955) of a restricted area in the hypothalamus can cause polydipsia. The fact that destructive lesions involving this same area may result in hypodipsia (STEVENSON 1949) or even adipsia (WITT, KELLER, BATSEL and LYNCH 1952, ANDERSSON and McCANN

[1] On leave from the Dept. of Neurophysiology, The Nencki Institute of Experimental Biology, Warsaw, Poland.

1956) gives further evidence that an essential "thirst centre" is located in the hypothalamus. It is possible that the stimulation of this "centre" produces a real sensation of thirst as during such experiments goats move actually towards the proffered water and drink (Andersson and McCann 1955 a). However, to get a more objective answer to the question whether or not the stimulation of the hypothalamic "drinking area" is connected with the active seeking for water, *i.e.* with the voluntary movements that will guarantee the water supply, the present study was undertaken.

METHODS

Two adult female goats were used for the experiments. At first the drinking of the animals was conditioned in such a way that they were taught to go up the two steps of a staircase placed in the experimental pen to get water. While training was in progress the goats were only allowed to drink during the actual training experiments in the pen and hence they were always thirsty when the daily routine started. The experimental pen, the staircase, and the experimenter standing in front of the staircase outside the pen, were the complex conditioned stimulus. The motor conditioned reactions developed during the period of training were such that one goat went up on to the first step with both her forelegs and then put her right hoof on the second step. The other goat climbed the staircase and assumed a standing position on its upper step. Each of these movements was immediately reinforced by giving the animals 100 ml of water to drink and the goats were taught to go down the steps after drinking. These motor reactions were thus elaborated by way of "passive movements" according to the method described by Konorski (1948).

The conditioned reaction appeared repeatedly at intervals of about 1 to 2 minutes. The daily experiment consisted of 10 to 15 trials. After about 14 days of training the conditioning of drinking was firmly established. Then, in the same conditioned situation, electrical stimulation within the "drinking area" of the hypothalamus was performed using Hess' technique (1932, 1949). The parameters of stimulation were 0.5—1V and 50 imp./sec. The stimulation experiments and some of the usual training experiments were filmed.

Histological technique: After the animals had been killed by decapitation the heads were perfused with Ringer's solution followed by Bodian's fixative and a block including the hypothalamus was cut out, imbedded in celloidin and cut in transverse sections, 100 microns thick. The sections were stained with toluidin blue to facilitate the localization of the points of stimulation.

RESULTS

When electrodes had been placed within the "drinking area" of the hypothalamus the previously trained animals were placed in the experimental pen where they could move freely. Some minutes later the usual conditioned reaction appeared and each attempt to find water was reinforced by giving water. After several trials the hitherto thirsty goats were allowed to drink water ad libitum following which the animals ceased completely to perform the learned movement, and refused to drink the water offered. Electrical stimulation of the "drinking area" was then applied, and was found to evoke the conditioned reaction followed by drinking of water. This effect was especially striking in one of the goats in which the effective point of stimulation was situated dorsally in the "drinking area" just lateral to the columna fornicis descendens (Fig. 1). Here the visible effect of a weak stimulation was "pure" polydipsia. The course of this stimulation experiment was the following.

Within 1 to 3 secs of the onset of stimulation (0.5 V), the goat went up the first step of the staircase and put her right foreleg on to the second step stamping impatiently on it with her hoof. When water then was offered she drank it in large gulps. As soon as the period of stimulation ended the goat suddenly stopped drinking, took her right leg off the upper step and went down on the floor of the pen. She thus exhibited exactly the same motor conditioned reaction as previously displayed during the period of training. Although the stimulation was repeated more than 20 times, at intervals from 10 secs to several minutes, it never failed to elicit the characteristic reaction. However, when in consequence of drinking during many periods of stimulation the goat gradually became overloaded with water, the latency of the conditioned reaction increased and the amount of water drunk during each period of stimulation became smaller.

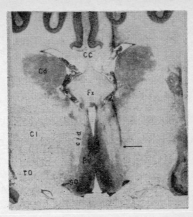

Fig. 1. *A transverse section through the anterior hypothalamus of the goat in which the drinking motor conditioned reaction was most efficiently elicited by electrical stimulation within the hypothalamic "drinking centre." The section is directed along the track of the effective electrode. The point of stimulation is indicated by the arrow.*

C.C.: *corpus callosum*	Fx : *fornix*
Cd : *N. Caudatus*	P.V.: *N. paraventricularis*
c.f.d.: *columna fornicis descendens*	S.O. : *N. supraopticus*
C.I. : *capsula interna*	T.O.: *tractus opticus*

At this time an increase of the strength of stimulation to 1V caused the reaction to grow stronger again. The amount of water drunk during the experiment was 6.5 liters. In the intervals between the stimulations the goat refused to drink the water offered and never performed the learned movements. Stimulation of other points in the diencephalon outside the "drinking area" did not elicit the conditioned reaction.

DISCUSSION

The results obtained show that the electrical stimulation of the hypothalamic "drinking centre" can elicit the motor conditioned reaction connected with drinking. In other words, the pattern of motor excitation seemingly established in the cerebral cortex as a result of previous training may be reproduced as a consequence of the stimulation of this "centre", which, thus, in terms of higher nervous activity, may be considered the origin of an unconditioned drinking reflex. This is in accordance with the suggestion, made by Wyrwicka (1952), on the basis of studies of alimentary motor conditioned reflexes, that the path of a motor conditioned reaction must run through the centre of the unconditioned reflex.

Some analogous data were reported by Grastyán, Lissák and Kékesi (1956) who found that an alimentary motor conditioned reflex could be elicited by the stimulation of some parts of the hypothalamus in cats. They interpreted this phenomenon as a non-specific facilitation of conditioned reflexes caused by the hypothalamic stimulation. As, however, it is possible that their stimulations involved an activation of the hypothalamic "feeding centre" (Brügger 1943, Anand and Brobeck 1951, Delgado and Anand 1953, Larsson 1954) their results may also be interpreted in the above mentioned way.

SUMMARY

When a drinking motor conditioned reaction was firmly established in goats it was possible to elicit the same reaction by electrical stimulation of the hypothalamic "drinking centre."

REFERENCES

Anand, B. K. and J. R. Brobeck, Proc. Soc. Biol. Med., 1951. 77. 323.

Andersson, B., Experientia, 1952. 8. 157.

—   Acta Physiol. Scand., 1953. 28. 188.

—   and S. M. McCann, Ibidem, 1955 a. 33. 333.

—   —   —   — , 1955 b. 35. 191.

—   —   —   — , 1956. 35. 312.

Brügger, M., Helv. Physiol. acta., 1943. 1. 183.

Delgado, J. M. and B. K. Anand, Amer. J. Physiol., 1953. 172. 162.

Grastyán, E., K. Lissák and F. Kékesi, Acta Physiol. Hung., 1956. 9. 133.

Greer, M. A., Proc. Soc. Exp. Biol., N. Y., 1955. 89 59.

Hess, W. R., Beiträge zur Physiologie des Hirnstammes I, Leipzig, George Thieme., 1932.

— Das Zwischenhirn, Basel: Schwabe, 1949.

Konorski, J., Conditioned reflexes and neuron organization, Cambridge: Univ. Press., 1948.

Larsson, S., Acta. Physiol. Scand., 1954. 32. Suppl. 115.

Stevenson, J. A. F., Recent Progr. Hormone Res., 1949. 4. 363.

Witt, D. M., A. D. Keller, H. L. Batsel, and J. R. Lynch, Amer. J. Physiol., 1952. 171. 780 P.

Wyrwicka, W., Acta Biol. Exper., 1952. 16. 131.

4

Glucostatic Mechanism of Regulation of Food Intake*

JEAN MAYER, PH.D., D.SC.†
Boston

The following selection raises the possibility that sugar receptors, which monitor the level of sugar in the blood, exist in the brain. It is presumed that small changes in blood sugar can cause changes in hypothalamic activity which produce the sensations of hunger or satiety. The activity is thought to mediate eating behavior and the cessation of the eating response. Such receptors have not, as yet, been isolated anatomically.

The article is reprinted from the New England Journal of Medicine, *1953, 249, 13-16, with the permission of the author and the journal.*

The regulation of energy intake is fundamental to all homeostatic mechanisms. Yet this basic process has received less attention than many of the physiologic regulations that it makes possible.

Before this century, three theories were advanced to account for the phenomenon of hunger. The theories of peripheral origin (Haller, Erasmus Darwin, Johannes Müller and Weber) held that the taking of food resulted

* From the Department of Nutrition, Harvard School of Public Health.

Supported in part by grants-in-aid from the National Institute of Arthritis and Metabolism and the National Heart Institute, National Institutes of Health, Public Health Service, Nutrition Foundation, Incorporated, New York City, Chemistry Scholarship Fund, New York City, National Biscuit Company, New York City, McCallum Foundation, Incorporated, New Brunswick, New Jersey, and Swift and Company, Chicago.

† Assistant professor of nutrition, Harvard School of Public Health.

from the stimulation either of all afferent nerves by some change in the tissues or of a strictly local group of sensory nerves, mainly in the stomach. The theory of central origin (Magendie, Tidewald and Milne-Edwards) postulated that a hunger center was sensitive to a starvation state of the blood. The theories of general sensation (Roux and Michael Foster) considered that the hunger center of the blood was stimulated not only by the hunger state of the blood but also indirectly by afferent impulses from all organs of the body.

After Cannon and Washburn, as well as Carlson, had shown that epigastric sensations of "hunger pain" coincided with waves of contractions of the empty stomach, Carlson[1] suggested that hypoglycemia, mediated by its effect on the stomach, might be responsible for inducing these hunger sensations. Although hunger pangs are found in most persons, the idea that the sensations elicited by stomach contractions due to hypoglycemia[2] were at the basis of the regulation of food intake was abandoned for the following reasons: it was repeatedly shown, in particular by Sherrington, that total denervation and surgical removal of the stomach did not fundamentally alter the characteristics of food intake regulation. Adolph[3] demonstrated, by diluting the ration of laboratory animals with inert material, that differences in the bulk of the diet had only a transient influence. Scott and his collaborators[4] were unable to correlate spontaneous fluctuations of blood sugar levels with a desire for food. The existence of diabetic hyperphagia and of the phenomenon of hunger diabetes also presented seemingly insurmountable difficulties. Even the increase in spontaneous intake due to insulin-induced hypoglycemia was held by some authors to be of no general significance because of the abnormal "unphysiologic" circumstances in which the organism was placed.[5]

The demonstration by Hetherington and Ranson[6] that destruction of parts of the medioventral nuclei of the hypothalamus leads to obesity and the work of Anand and Brobeck[7] showing that more lateral lesions cause anorexia reopened the problem of the nature of the physiologic mechanism of the regulation of food intake.

Experimental work on rats, mice, dogs and human subjects culminated in the proposal of a "glucostatic mechanism" of regulation of food intake.[8-10] The initial reasoning was as follows: the regulation of food intake proceeds by relatively frequent partaking of food (meals). It appears improbable that hypothalamic centers are sensitive to decrease of the body content in fat or protein—during the short interval between meals, this decrease is proportionally very small. On the other hand, the body stores of carbohydrate are limited. The postprandial liver glycogen content in man is approximately 75 gm.—only 300 calories' worth. In the postabsorptive period, in spite of gluconeogenesis (the synthesizing of glycogen from body proteins), glycogen stores become rapidly depleted. This synthesis of glycogen from proteins and the shifting of metabolic oxidation in non-nervous tissues from glucose to fat (as measured by the lowering of the respiratory quotient) tend to minimize the drop in blood glucose resulting from depletion of liver glycogen stores. Thus, minimum levels necessary for the survival of the central nervous system are maintained. Only partaking of food, however, can restore full homeostasis of the central nervous system. It appeared, as a working hypothesis, that the central nervous system, dependent exclusively on a continued supply of glucose in blood, should maintain "glucoreceptors" sensitive to fluctuations of available blood glucose. (That glucoreceptors do in fact exist in the central nervous system has been implicitly recognized by surgeons; a common method for testing the completeness of vagotomies consists in administering insulin and ascertaining that the resultant hypoglycemia fails to elicit or delays gastric secretion of hydrochloric acid.)* In this "glucostatic" view, hunger would be integrated among the mechanisms through which the central nervous system ensures its homeostasis.

A first (and rather crude) test of this hypothesis was provided by a systematic survey of the effect of administration of various metabolites[9] on the food intakes of groups of normal animals. Increases in levels of reducing

---

* This phenomenon was recently analyzed experimentally by Porter et al.[11] It was shown specifically that in monkeys the anterior hypothalamus was responsible for the secretion of hydrochloric acid after insulin administration.

sugar in blood were obtained by injections of glucose or
fructose or small doses of epinephrine. Decreases were
obtained by injections of small, graded doses of insulin.
Levels below normal fasting values were avoided, so as to
stay within physiologic limits. The effects of the injection
of substances without influence on blood glucose levels,
like sucrose and fat emulsions, were also studied. It was
found that temporary increases in blood glucose levels
corresponded to decreases in food intake and vice versa,
even when the caloric equivalent of injected metabolites
was taken into account. Substances without effect on
blood glucose did not influence food intake over and
beyond caloric value, if they were metabolizable. Although significant, variations in food intake induced by
these variations in blood sugar were small because of the
efficiency of homeostatic mechanisms concerned with
blood glucose levels. To demonstrate more clearly the
inhibitory effect of high blood glucose levels on food intake, animals of the "Houssay" type, in this case alloxan-
treated hypophysectomized rats, were injected with glucose.[9] (Although these animals do not normally present
hyperglycemia, they have been deprived of the mechanisms that ensure the rapid removal of injected glucose;
hyperglycemia can thus be conveniently maintained for
a much longer period.) Two daily glucose injections were
found to reduce food intake by half; three such injections, maintaining hyperglycemia around the clock, caused
death of these animals from inanition in spite of the
presence of food in their cage.

The apparent paradoxes afforded by the hyperphagia
of diabetes mellitus, by the phenomenon of hunger diabetes, in which a previously fasted person will continue
to eat in spite of a blood glucose reaching abnormally
high levels, by the hyperphagia accompanying tendency
to higher glucose levels in the obese, still had to be resolved before it could be concluded that blood glucose
levels regulate food intake. It appears that all these conditions may have one factor in common—namely, that
whereas absolute levels of blood glucose are increased,
utilization is decreased. For variations of blood sugar
levels to influence hypothalamic glucoreceptors, glucose
has to cross the membranes of these cells. This presum-

ably implies phosphorylation through the hexokinase reaction. If phosphorylation is impaired, "effective sugar levels" will be in fact lower than absolute values as measured.

This concept was tested and put on a quantitative basis in a series of experiments performed on human subjects.[10, 12] Because of the inaccessibility of the hypothalamic centers, peripheral arteriovenous differences were determined as an index of rates of glucose utilization. These differences (designated as "Δ-glucose") were measured in the antecubital region (between finger blood and antecubital-vein blood). With one exception, discussed in some detail below, Δ-glucose values were found to correlate closely with the caloric intake of the subject and with hunger feelings (Fig. 1).

Diets calorically adequate were associated with Δ-glucose values that remained large[8] throughout the day, decreasing only at mealtime. By contrast, submaintenance diets were followed by rapid shrinkage of Δ-glucose after meals; at the same time, hunger returned. When hunger diabetes was present, blood glucose values rose until a difference appeared between arterial and venous levels—only then was hunger assuaged. Generally speaking, there appeared to be a quantitative relation between food intake and the area represented by the Δ-glucose as a function of time. There was also a quantitative relation between Δ-glucose values and the incidence of hunger feelings; antecubital arteriovenous differences of more than 15 mg. per 100 cc. were never associated with hunger; values staying near 0 for any length of time were always associated with hunger.

In uncontrolled diabetes mellitus, a similar picture was obtained; blood sugar values had to be forced up through ingestion of food to levels where arteriovenous differences were introduced for ravenous hunger feelings to be satisfied. Cortisone administration accompanied by increased appetite caused an elevation of absolute glucose levels but a decrease in Δ-glucose.

The effect of epinephrine deserves special mention since it represents an apparent exception to the general rule. Administration of epinephrine caused an immediate increase in blood glucose; it drastically reduced or elimi-

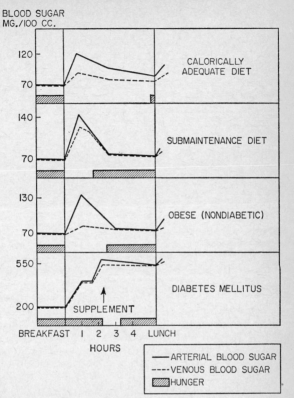

Fig. 1. *Typical morning correlations of Δ-glucose and hunger feeling. The size of the Δ-glucose (peripheral glucose arteriovenous difference) correlates with hunger feelings. No hunger feeling appears if the Δ-glucose is greater than 10 mg. per 100 cc.*

nated any effect of hunger. However, at the same time, it decreased peripheral Δ-glucose to levels near 0. Although it may be an oversimplification to ascribe this seeming contradiction to one of the many physiologic effects of epinephrine, it is worth noting that epinephrine introduces a differential between peripheral and central blood flow.[13] By the same token, experiments conducted on animals demonstrate that, whereas it decreases peripheral Δ-glucose values, it increases carotid-jugular glucose differences; thus it not only produces hyperglycemia but also increases the proportion of glucose made available to the nervous centers.*

Insulin treatment first causes a fall in blood sugar owing to increased peripheral utilization of glucose. In a second phase, a compensatory rise takes place that is secondary to decreased utilization of glucose in the periphery.[15] Delta glucose values rapidly decline when the blood sugar falls to or below post-absorptive levels. The occurrence of increased hunger after insulin administration is therefore easily interpreted if hunger is seen as a direct response to carbohydrate deprivation.

In hyperthyroidism, alimentary hyperglycemia typically occurs and is followed regularly by a postalimentary hypoglycemia. It has been suggested[16] that accelerated metabolism of glucose takes place in the hyperthyroid patient and that the alimentary hyperglycemia may be only a manifestation of starvation diabetes that follows rapid depletion of carbohydrate stores. It appears that the metabolic hypoglycemia of hyperthyroidism may thus be related to the increased food intake characteristic of this condition.**

The possibility that the "feeding centers" in the lateral hypothalamus represent the sensitive area with facilitatory properties in terms of eating mechanisms has been discussed by Brobeck.[18] † In the glucostatic view proposed here these centers would represent the glucoreceptors. There is an obvious need for a mechanism that would translate available blood glucose into variations in the physiologic state of the tissues. Such a mechanism is suggested by the observation that a drop in serum inorganic phosphate and in potassium consistently accompanies large Δ-glucose values.[12, 20, 21] It is possible that the passage of potassium ions into the glucoreceptor

---

* Keller and Roberts[14] recently demonstrated that glucose consumption of hypothalamic tissue is increased in vitro within a few minutes of the administration of epinephrine.

** It has recently been shown[17] that, in the cold, carbohydrate metabolism is also accelerated and glycogen reserves are decreased. A similar situation is known to prevail in growth.

† It was later demonstrated that electric stimulation of this lateral area causes an increase in food intake.[19]

cells along with the glucose phosphate represents the point at which effective glucose level is translated into an electric or neural mechanism.

It is recognized that hypothalamic impulses still have to be interpreted, integrated and acted upon by the cerebral cortex; that other afferent impulses (gastric hunger pangs, in particular) also play a role in determining conscious states of hunger; and that other psychologic and physiologic factors may intervene to modify appetite at least temporarily. Conditioned reflexes, particularly in the dog, and habits in man also play an important role. Still, although feelings involving desire for food or satiety are not in any sense quantifiable, they represent a conscious expression of one of the most precise regulatory devices in biology. The glucostatic mechanism suggested here seems to provide a basis for such a precise regulation. It may be added that, because of the established decrease by available glucose of the rate of fat [22] and amino acid [23] utilization in non-nervous tissue, and probably of the rate of gluconeogenesis as well,[24] the regulation of food intake is easily integrated into the general regulation of metabolism.

Finally, it may be noted that the glucostatic theory seems to permit interpretation of certain types of alteration of the regulation of energy intake, in particular hypothalamic obesity,[25] the hereditary obese hyperglycemic syndrome of mice[26] and at least one form of human obesity.[27] The demonstration[28] that, in the hereditary obese-hyperglycemic syndrome of mice, the alpha cells of the islands of Langerhans oversecrete a hormone with hyperglycemic, glycogenolytic and antiinsulin properties opens the possibility that this hormone plays a major role in the regulation of food intake and in the etiology of obesity.

The broadening of the initial theory and its application to special cases were evolved in collaboration with Dr. T. B. Van Itallie, for two years a member of the Department of Nutrition, Harvard School of Public Health, and now at St. Luke's Hospital, New York City. The work summarized here was done with the collaboration of Dr. Rachel Beaudoin, a former graduate student in the Department, now at the University of Montreal, and of Miss Margaret Bates, also a graduate student. I am also indebted to Dr. Fredrick J. Stare, head of the Department, for his constant support, interest and encouragement.

REFERENCES

1. Carlson, A. J. *The Control of Hunger in Health and Disease.* 320 pp. Chicago: University of Chicago Press, 1916.
2. Bulatao, E., and Carlson, A. J. Contributions to physiology of stomach: influence of experimental changes in blood-sugar level on gastric hunger contractions. *Am. J. Physiol.* 59:107-115, 1924.
3. Adolph, E. F. Urges to eat and drink in rats. *Am. J. Physiol.* 151:110-125, 1947.
4. Scott, W. W., Scott, C. C., and Luckhardt, A. B. Observations on blood sugar level before, during and after hunger periods in humans. *Am. J. Physiol.* 123:243-247, 1938.
5. Janowitz, H. D., and Grossman, M. I. Hunger and appetite: some definitions and concepts. *J. Mt. Sinai Hosp.* 16:231-240, 1949.
6. Hetherington, A. W., and Ranson, S. W. Hypothalamic lesions and adiposity in rat. *Anat. Rec.* 78:149-172, 1940.
7. Anand, B. K., and Brobeck, J. R. Localization of "feeding center" in hypothalamus of rat. *Proc. Soc. Exper. Biol. & Med.* 77:323, 1951.
8. Mayer, J., and Bates, M. W. Mechanism of regulation of food intake. *Federation Proc.* 10:389, 1951.
9. *Idem.* Blood glucose and food intake in normal and hypophysectomized, alloxan-treated rats. *Am. J. Physiol.* 168:812-819, 1952.
10. Mayer, J. Glucostatic theory of regulation of food intake and problem of obesity. *Bull. New England M. Center* 14:43-49, 1952.
11. Porter, R. W., Longmire, R. L., and French, J. D. Neurohumoral influence on gastric hydrochloric acid secretion. *Federation Proc.* 12:110, 1953.
12. Van Itallie, T. B., Beaudoin, R., and Mayer, J. Arteriovenous glucose differences, metabolic hypoglycemia and food intake in man. *J. Clin. Nutrition* 1:208-217, 1953.
13. Somogyi, M. Studies of arteriovenous differences in blood sugar. Effect of epinephrine on rate of glucose utilization. *J. Biol. Chem.* 186:513-526, 1950.
14. Keller, M. R., and Roberts, S. Epinephrine stimulation of pituitary metabolism. *Federation Proc.* 12:76, 1953.

15. Somogyi, M. Effect of insulin hypoglycemia on alimentary hyperglycemia. *J. Biol. Chem.* 193:859-871, 1951.

16. Peters, J. P., and Van Slyke, D. D. *Quantitative Clinical Chemistry*. Vol. 1. Interpretations. 1041 pp. Baltimore: Williams and Wilkins, 1946. P. 328.

17. Baker, D. G., and Sellers, E. A. Carbohydrate metabolism in rat exposed to low environmental temperature. *Federation Proc.* 12:8, 1953.

18. Brobeck, J. R. Physiology of appetite. In *Overeating, Overweight and Obesity: Proceeedings of the Nutrition Symposium held at the Harvard School of Public Health, Boston, October 29, 1952.* 151 pp. New York: National Vitamin Foundation, 1953. Pp. 36-51.

19. Delgado, J. M. R., and Anand, B. K. Increase of food intake induced by electrical stimulation of lateral hypothalamus. *Am. J. Physiol.* 172:162-168, 1953.

20. McCullagh, D. R., and Van Alstine, L. Phosphates in sugar tolerance test. *Am. J. Clin. Path.* 2:277-287, 1932.

21. Levine, R., Loube, S. D., and Weisberg, H. F. Nature of action of insulin on level of serum inorganic phosphate. *Am. J. Physiol.* 159:107-110, 1949.

22. Geyer, R. P., Bowie, E. J., and Bates, J. C. Effects of fasting and pyruvate on palmitic acid metabolism. *J. Biol. Chem.* 200:271-274, 1953.

23. Winzler, R. J., Moldave, K., Rafelson, M. E., Jr., and Pearson, H. E. Conversion of glucose to amino acids by brain and liver of newborn mouse. *J. Biol. Chem.* 199: 485-492, 1952.

24. Engel, F. L., Schiller, S., and Pentz, E. I. Studies on nature of protein catabolic response to adrenal cortical extract. *Endocrinology* 44:458-475, 1949.

25. Mayer, J., Bates, M. W., and Van Itallie, T. B. Blood sugar and food intake in rats with lesions of anterior hypothalamus. *Metabolism* 1:340-348, 1952.

26. Mayer, J., Russell, R. E., Bates, M. W., and Dickie, M. M. Metabolic, nutritional and endocrine studies of hereditary obesity-diabetes syndrome of mice and mechanism of its development. *Metabolism* 2:9-21, 1953.

27. Beaudoin, R., Van Itallie, T. B., and Mayer, J. Carbohydrate metabolism in "active" and "static" human obesity. *J. Clin. Nutrition* 1:91-99, 1953.

28. Mayer, J., Silides, D. N., and Bates, M. W. Possible role of pancreatic alpha cells in hereditary obese-hyperglycemic syndrome of mice. *Federation Proc.* 12:423, 1953.

5

Positive Reinforcement Produced by Electrical Stimulation of Septal Area and Other Regions of Rat Brain[1]

JAMES OLDS[2] AND PETER MILNER
McGill University

The following selection represents a major contribution to the study of behavior. It demonstrates, in the operationally unmotivated organism, that instrumental responses may be reinforced by electrical stimulation of the brain. Prior to this discovery, it was believed that learning could only be demonstrated by producing a state of need such as hunger and by presenting a food reward to the animal following the performance of a correct response. The relation between food reward to a hungry animal and brain stimulation is yet to be determined, although it is clear that both can modify behavior.

The following selection is reprinted from The Journal of Comparative and Physiological Psychology, 1954, 47, 419-427 *with the permission of the authors and the American Psychological Association.*

[1] The research reported here was made possible by grants from the Rockefeller Foundation and the National Institute of Mental Health of the U.S. Public Health Service. The authors particularly wish to express their thanks to Professor D. O. Hebb, who provided germinal ideas for the research and who backed it with enthusiastic encouragement as well as laboratory facilities and funds. The authors are also grateful to Miss Joann Feindel, who performed the histological reconstructions reported here.

[2] National Institute of Mental Health Postdoctorate Fellow of the U.S. Public Health Service.

Stimuli have eliciting and reinforcing functions. In studying the former, one concentrates on the responses which come after the stimulus. In studying the latter, one looks mainly at the responses which precede it. In its reinforcing capacity, a stimulus increases, decreases, or leaves unchanged the frequency of preceding responses, and accordingly it is called a reward, a punishment, or a neutral stimulus (cf. 16).

Previous studies using chronic implantation of electrodes have tended to focus on the eliciting functions of electrical stimuli delivered to the brain (2, 3, 4, 5, 7, 10, 12, 14). The present study, on the other hand, has been concerned with the reinforcing function of the electrical stimulation.[3]

METHOD

GENERAL

Stimulation was carried out by means of chronically implanted electrodes which did not interfere with the health or free behavior of Ss to any appreciable extent. The Ss were 15 male hooded rats, weighing approximately 250 gm. at the start of the experiment. Each S was tested in a Skinner box which delivered alternating current to the brain so long as a lever was depressed. The current was delivered over a loose lead, suspended from the ceiling, which connected the stimulator to the rat's electrode. The Ss were given a total of 6 to 12 hr. of acquisition testing, and 1 to 2 hr. of extinction testing. During acquisition, the stimulator was turned on so that a response produced electrical stimulation; during extinction, the stimulator was turned off so that a response produced no electrical stimulation. Each S was given a percentage score denoting the proportion of his total acquisition time given to responding. This score could be compared with the animal's extinction score to determine whether the stimulation had a positive, negative, or neutral reinforcing effect. After testing, the animal was sacrificed. Its brain was frozen, sectioned, stained, and examined microscopically to determine which structure of the brain had been stimulated. This permitted correlation of acquisition scores with anatomical structures.

[3] The present preliminary paper deals mainly with methods and behavioral results. A detailed report of the locus of positive, negative, and neutral reinforcing effects of electrical brain stimulation is being prepared by the first author.

ELECTRODE IMPLANTATION

Electrodes are constructed by cementing a pair of enameled silver wires of 0.010-in. diameter into a Lucite block, as shown in Fig. 1. The parts of the wires which penetrate the brain are

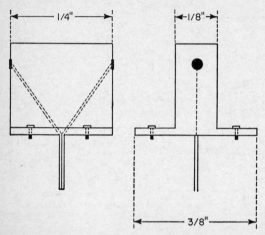

Fig. 1. Electrode design (see text for detailed description).

cemented together to form a needle, and this is cut to the correct length to reach the desired structure in the brain. This length is determined from Krieg's rat brain atlas (11) with slight modifications as found necessary by experience. The exposed cross section of the wire is the only part of the needle not insulated from the brain by enamel; stimulation therefore occurs only at the tip. Contact with the lead from the stimulator is made through two blobs of solder on the upper ends of the electrode wires; these blobs make contact with the jaws of an alligator clip which has been modified to insulate the two jaws from one another. A light, flexible hearing-aid lead connects the clip to the voltage source.

The operation of implantation is performed with the rat under Nembutal anesthesia (0.88 cc/Kg) and held in a Johnson-Krieg stereotaxic instrument (11). A mid-line incision is made in the scalp and the skin held out of the way by muscle retractors. A small hole is drilled in the skull with a dental burr at the point indicated by the stereotaxic instrument for the structure it is desired to stimulate. The electrode, which is clamped into the needle carrier of the instrument, is lowered until the flange of the Lucite block rests firmly on the skull. Four screw holes are then drilled in the skull through four fixing holes in the flange, and the electrode, still clamped firmly in the instrument, is fastened to the skull with jeweler's screws which exceed the diameter of the screw holes in the skull by 0.006 in. The electrode is then released from the clamp and the scalp wound closed with silk sutures. The skin is pulled tightly around the base of the Lucite block and kept well away from the contact plates. A recovery period of three days is allowed after the operation before testing. Figure 2 is an X-ray picture of an electrode in place.

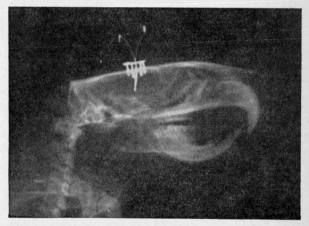

Fig. 2. X-ray showing electrode in place in intact animal. There are two wires insulated completely from each other, stimulating the brain with their tips.

TESTING

The testing apparatus consisted of a large-levered Skinner box 11 in. long, 5 in. wide, and 12 in. high. The top was open to allow passage for the stimulating lead. The lever actuated a microswitch in the stimulating circuit so that when it was depressed, the rat received electrical stimulation. The current was obtained from the 60-cycle power line, through a step-down transformer, and was adjustable between 0 and 10 v. r.m.s. by means of a variable potentiometer. In the experiments described here the stimulation continued as long as the lever was pressed, though for some tests a time-delay switch was incorporated which cut the current off after a predetermined interval if the rat continued to hold the lever down. Responses were recorded automatically on paper strip.

On the fourth day after the operation rats were given a pretesting session of about an hour in the boxes. Each rat was placed in the box and on the lever by E with the stimulus set at 0.5 v. During the hour, stimulation voltage was varied to determine the threshold of a "just noticeable" effect on the rat's behavior. If the animal did not respond regularly from the start, it was placed on the lever periodically (at about 5-min. intervals). Data collected on the first day were not used in later calculations. On subsequent days, Ss were placed in the box for about $3\frac{1}{2}$ hr. a day; these were 3 hr. of acquisition and $\frac{1}{2}$ hr. of extinction. During the former, the rats were allowed to stimulate themselves with a voltage which was just high enough to produce some noticeable response in the resting animal. As this threshold voltage fluctuated with the passage of time, E would make a determination of it every half hour, unless S was responding regularly. At the beginning of each acquisition period, and after each voltage test, the animal was placed on the lever once by E. During extinction periods, conditions were precisely the same except that a bar press produced no electrical stimulation. At the beginning of each extinction period, animals which were not responding regularly were placed on the lever once by E. At first, rats were tested in this way for four days, but as there appeared to be little difference between the results on different days, this period was reduced to three and then to two days for subsequent animals. Thus, the first rats had about 12 hr. of acquisition after pretesting whereas later rats had about 6 hr. However, in computing the scores in our table, we have used only the first 6 hr. of acquisition for all animals, so the scores are strictly comparable. In behavioral curves, we have shown the full 12 hr. of acquisition on the earlier animals so as to illustrate the stability of the behavior over time.

At no time during the experiment were the rats deprived of food or water, and no reinforcement was used except the electrical stimulus.

Animals were scored on the percentage of time which they spent bar pressing regularly during acquisition. In order to find how much time the animal would spend in the absence of reward or punishment, a similar score was computed for periods of extinction. This extinction score provided a base line. When the acquisition score is above the extinction score, we have reward; when it is below the extinction score, we have punishment.

In order to determine percentage scores, periods when the animal was responding regularly (at least one response every 30 sec.) were counted as periods of responding; i.e., *intervals of 30 sec. or longer without a response were counted as periods of no responding.* The percentage scores were computed as the proportion of total acquisition or extinction time given to periods of responding.

DETERMINATION OF LOCUS

On completion of testing, animals were perfused with physiological saline, followed by 10 per cent formalin. The brains were removed, and after further fixation in formalin for about a week, frozen sections 40 microns thick were cut through the region of the electrode track. These were stained with cresyl violet and the position of the electrode tip determined. Figure 3 is a photomicrograph showing the appearance of the electrode track in a stained and mounted brain section.

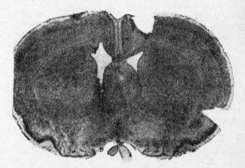

Fig. 3. Photomicrograph showing the electrode track in a cresyl-violet-stained brain section. The section is 1 mm. in front of the anterior commissure. The electrode protruded through the lateral ventricle and its stimulating tip was in the septal area.

RESULTS

LOCUS

In Table 1, acquisition and extinction scores are correlated with electrode placements. Figure 4 presents the acquisition scores again, this time on three cross-sectional maps of the rat brain, one at the forebrain level, one at the thalamic level, and one at the mid-brain level. The

TABLE 1

Acquisition and Extinction Scores for All Animals Together with Electrode Placements and Threshold Voltages Used during Acquisition Tests

Animal's No.	Locus of Electrode	Stimulation Voltage r.m.s.	Percentage of Acquisition Time Spent Responding	Percentage of Extinction Time Spent Responding
32	septal	2.2–2.8	75	18
34	septal	1.4	92	6
M-1	septal	1.7–4.8	85	21
M-4	septal	2.3–4.8	88	13
40	c.c.	.7–1.1	6	3
41	caudate	.9–1.2	4	4
31	cingulate	1.8	37	9
82	cingulate	.5–1.8	36	10
36	hip.	.8–2.8	11	14
3	m.l.	.5	0	4
A-5	m.t.	1.4	71	9
6	m.g.	.5	0	31
11	m.g.	.5	0	21
17	teg.	.7	2	1
9	teg.	.5	77	81

KEY: *c.c.*, *corpus callosum*; *hip.*, hippocampus; *m.l.*, medial lemniscus; *m.t.*, Mammillothalamic tract; *m.g.*, medial geniculate; *teg.*, tegmentum.

position of a score on the map indicates the electrode placement from which this acquisition score was obtained.

The highest scores are found together in the central portion of the forebrain. Beneath the *corpus callosum* and between the two lateral ventricles in section I of Fig. 4, we find four acquisition scores ranging from 75 to 92 per cent. This is the septal area. The Ss which produced these scores are numbered 32, 34, M-1, and M-4 in Table 1. It will be noticed that while all of them spent more than 75 per cent of their acquisition time responding, they all spent less than 22 per cent of their extinction time responding. Thus the electrical stimulus in the septal area has an effect which is apparently equivalent to that of a conventional primary reward as far as the maintenance of a lever-pressing response is concerned.

If we move outside the septal area, either in the direction of the caudate nucleus (across the lateral ventricle) or in the direction of the *corpus callosum*, we find acquisition scores drop abruptly to levels of from 4 to 6

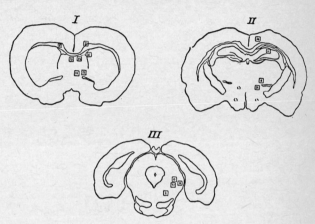

Fig. 4. *Maps of three sections*, (I) *through the forebrain*, (II) *through the thalamus*, (III) *through the mid-brain of the rat. Boxed numbers give acquisition percentage scores produced by animals with electrodes stimulating at these points. On section* I *the acquisition scores 75, 88, 92, 85 fall in the septal forebrain area. On the same section there is a score of 4 in the caudate nucleus, a score of 6 in the white matter below the cortex, and a score of 37 in the medial (cingulate) cortex. On section* II *the acquisition score of 36 is in the medial (cingulate) cortex, 11 is in the hippocampus, 71 is in the mammillothalamic tract, and 0 is in the medial lemniscus. On section* III *the two zeroes are in the medial geniculate, 2 is in the tegmental reticular substance, 77 falls 2 mm. anterior to the section shown—it is between the posterior commissure and the red nucleus.*

per cent. These are definitely indications of neutral (neither rewarding nor punishing) effects.

However, above the *corpus callosum* in the cingulate cortex we find an acquisition score of 37 per cent. As the extinction score in this case was 9 per cent, we may say that stimulation was rewarding.

At the thalamic level (section II of Fig. 4) we find a

36 per cent acquisition score produced by an electrode placed again in the cingulate cortex, an 11 per cent score produced by an electrode placed in the hippocampus, a 71 per cent score produced by an electrode placed exactly in the mammillothalamic tract, and a zero per cent score produced by an electrode placed in the medial lemniscus. The zero denotes negative reinforcement.

At the mid-brain level (section III of Fig. 4) there are two zero scores produced by electrodes which are in the posterior portion of the medial geniculate bodies; here again, the scores indicate a negative effect, as the corresponding extinction scores are 31 and 21 per cent. There is an electrode deep in the medial, posterior tegmentum which produces a 2 per cent score; this seems quite neutral, as the extinction score in this case is 1 per cent. Finally, there is an electrode shown on this section which actually stands 1½ mm. anterior at the point where it is shown; it was between the red nucleus and the posterior commissure. It produced an acquisition score of 77 per cent, but an extinction score of 81 per cent. This must be a rewarding placement, but the high extinction score makes it difficult to interpret.

BEHAVIOR

We turn our attention briefly to the behavioral data produced by the more rewarding electrode placements.

The graph in Fig. 5 is a smoothed cumulative response curve illustrating the rate of responding of rat No. 32 (the lowest-scoring septal area rat) during acquisition and extinction. The animal gave a total of slightly over 3000 responses in the 12 hr. of acquisition. When the current was turned on, the animal responded at a rate of 285 responses an hour; when the current was turned off, the rate fell close to zero.

The graph in Fig. 6 gives similar data on rat No. 34 (the highest-scoring septal rat). The animal stimulated itself over 7500 times in 12 hr. Its average response rate during acquisition was 742 responses an hour; during extinction, practically zero.

Figure 7 presents an unsmoothed cumulative response curve for one day of responding for rat No. A-5. This is to illustrate in detail the degree of control exercised by the electrical reward stimulus. While this rat was actually bar pressing, it did so at 1920 responses an hour; that is, about one response for every 2 sec. During the first period of the day it responded regularly while on acquisition,

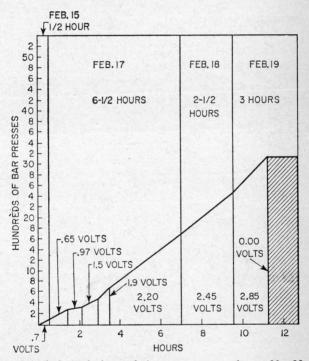

Fig. 5. Smoothed cumulative response curve for rat No. 32. Cumulative response totals are given along the ordinate, and hours along the abscissa. The steepness of the slope indicates the response rate. Stimulating voltages are given between black lines. Cross hatching indicates extinction.

extinguished very rapidly when the current was turned off, and reconditioned readily when the current was turned on again. At reconditioning points, E gave S one stimulus to show that the current was turned on again,

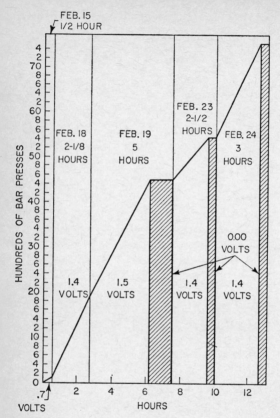

Fig. 6. Smoothed cumulative response curve for rat No. 34.

but E did not place S on the lever. During longer periods
of acquisition, S occasionally stopped responding for short
periods, but in the long run S spent almost three-quarters
of its acquisition time responding. During the long period of extinction at the end of the day, there was very
little responding, but S could be brought back to the
lever quite quickly if a stimulus was delivered to show
that the current had been turned on again.

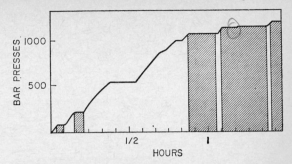

Fig. 7. *Unsmoothed cumulative response curve showing about ¾ hr. of acquisition and ¾ hr. extinction for rat No. A-5. Shading indicates extinction.*

DISCUSSION

It is clear that electrical stimulation in certain parts of the brain, particularly the septal area, produces acquisition and extinction curves which compare favorably with those produced by a conventional primary reward. With other electrode placements, the stimulation appears to be neutral or punishing.

Because the rewarding effect has been produced maximally by electrical stimulation in the septal area, but also in lesser degrees in the mammillothalamic tract and cingulate cortex, we are led to speculate that a system of structures previously attributed to the rhinencephalon may provide the locus for the reward phenomenon. However, as localization studies which will map the whole brain with respect to the reward and punishment dimension are continuing, we will not discuss in detail the problem of locus. We will use the term "reinforcing structures" in further discussion as a general name for the septal area and other structures which produce the reward phenomenon.

To provide an adequate canvass of the possible explanations for the rewarding effect would require considerably more argument than could possibly fit within the confines of a research paper. We have decided, therefore, to rule out briefly the possibility that the implantation produces pain which is reduced by electrical stimulation of reinforcing structures, and to confine further discussion to suggestions of ways the phenomenon may provide a methodological basis for study of physiological mechanisms of reward.

The possibility that the implantation produces some painful "drive stimulus" which is alleviated by electrical stimulation of reinforcing structures does not comport with the facts which we have observed. If there were some chronic, painful drive state, it would be indicated by emotional signs in the animal's daily behavior. Our Ss, from the first day after the operation, are normally quiet, nonaggressive; they eat regularly, sleep regularly, gain weight. There is no evidence in their behavior to support the postulation of chronic pain. Septal preparations which have lived healthy and normal lives for months after the operation have given excellent response rates.

As there is no evidence of a painful condition preceding the electrical stimulation, and as the animals are given free access to food and water at all times except while actually in the Skinner boxes, there is no explicitly manipulated drive to be reduced by electrical stimulation. Barring the possibility that stimulation of a reinforcing structure specifically inhibits the "residual drive" state of the animal, or the alternative possibility that the first electrical stimulus has noxious after-effects which are reduced by a second one, we have some evidence here for a primary rewarding effect which is not associated with the reduction of a primary drive state. It is perhaps fair in a discussion to report the "clinical impression" of the Es that the phenomenon represents strong pursuit of a positive stimulus rather than escape from some negative condition.

Should the latter interpretation prove correct, we have perhaps located a system within the brain whose peculiar function is to produce a rewarding effect on behavior. The location of such a system puts us in a position to collect information that may lead to a decision among conflicting theories of reward. By physiological studies, for example, we may find that the reinforcing structures act selectively on sensory or motor areas of the cortex.

This would have relevance to current S-S versus S-R controversies (8, 9, 13, 16).

Similarly, extirpation studies may show whether reinforcing structures have primarily a quieting or an activating effect on behavior; this would be relevant to activation versus negative feedback theories of reward (6, 13, 15, 17). A recent study by Brady and Nauta (1) already suggests that the septal area is a quieting system, for its surgical removal produced an extremely active animal.

Such examples, we believe, make it reasonable to hope that the methodology reported here should have important consequences for physiological studies of mechanisms of reward.

SUMMARY

A preliminary study was made of rewarding effects produced by electrical stimulation of certain areas of the brain. In all cases rats were used and stimulation was by 60-cycle alternating current with voltages ranging from ½ to 5 v. Bipolar needle electrodes were permanently implanted at various points in the brain. Animals were tested in Skinner boxes where they could stimulate themselves by pressing a lever. They received no other reward than the electrical stimulus in the course of the experiments. The primary findings may be listed as follows: (a) There are numerous places in the lower centers of the brain where electrical stimulation is rewarding in the sense that the experimental animal will stimulate itself in these places frequently and regularly for long periods of time if permitted to do so. (b) It is possible to obtain these results from as far back as the tegmentum, and as far forward as the septal area; from as far down as the subthalamus, and as far up as the cingulate gyrus of the cortex. (c) There are also sites in the lower centers where the effect is just the opposite: animals do everything possible to avoid stimulation. And there are neutral sites: animals do nothing to obtain or to avoid stimulation. (d) The reward results are obtained more dependably with electrode placements in some areas than others, the septal area being the most dependable to date. (e) In septal area preparations, the control exercised over the animal's behavior by means of this reward is extreme, possibly exceeding that exercised by any other reward previously used in animal experimentation.

The possibility that the reward results depended on some chronic painful consequences of the implantation operation was ruled out on the evidence that no physiological or behavioral signs of such pain could be found. The phenomenon was discussed as possibly laying a methodological foundation for a physiological study of the mechanisms of reward.

REFERENCES

1. BRADY, J. V., & NAUTA, W. J. H. Subcortical mechanisms in emotional behavior: affective changes following septal forebrain lesions in the albino rat. *J. comp. physiol. Psychol.*, 1953, 46, 339-346.
2. DELGADO, J. M. R. Permanent implantation of multilead electrodes in the brain. *Yale J. Biol. Med.*, 1952, 24, 351-358.
3. DELGADO, J. M. R. Responses evoked in waking cat by electrical stimulation of motor cortex. *Amer. J. Physiol.*, 1952, 171, 436-446.
4. DELGADO, J. M. R., & ANAND, B. K. Increase of food intake induced by electrical stimulation of the lateral hypothalamus. *Amer. J. Physiol.*, 1953, 172, 162-168.
5. DELL, P. Correlations entre le système vegetatif et le système de la vie relation: mesencephale, diencephale, et cortex cerebral. *J. Physiol.* (Paris), 1952, 44, 471-557.
6. DEUTSCH, J. A. A new type of behavior theory. *Brit. J. Psychol.*, 1953, 44, 304-317.
7. GASTAUT, H. Correlations entre le système nerveux vegetatif et le système de la vie de relation dans le rhinencephale. *J. Physiol.* (Paris), 1952, 44, 431-470.
8. HEBB, D .O. *The organization of behavior.* New York: Wiley, 1949.
9. HULL, C. L. *Principles of behavior.* New York: D. Appleton-Century, 1943.
10. HUNTER, J., & JASPER, H. H. Effects of thalamic stimulation in unanaesthetized animals. *EEG clin. Neurophysiol.*, 1949, 1, 305-324.
11. KRIEG, W. J. S. Accurate placement of minute lesions in

the brain of the albino rat. *Quart. Bull., Northwestern Univer. Med. School*, 1946, 20, 199-208.

12. MacLean, P. D., & Delgado, J. M. R. Electrical and chemical stimulation of frontotemporal portion of limbic system in the waking animal. *EEG clin. Neurophysiol.*, 1953, 5, 91-100.

13. Olds, J. A neural model for sign-gestalt theory. *Psychol. Rev.*, 1954, 61, 59-72.

14. Rosvold, H. E., & Delgado, J. M. R. The effect on the behavior of monkeys of electrically stimulating or destroying small areas within the frontal lobes. *Amer. Psychologist*, 1953, 8, 425-426. (Abstract)

15. Seward, J. P. Introduction to a theory of motivation in learning. *Psychol. Rev.*, 1952, 59, 405-413.

16. Skinner, B. F. *The behavior of organisms.* New York: D. Appleton-Century, 1938.

17. Wiener, N. *Cybernetics.* New York: Wiley, 1949.

Part II

The Relation Between Deprivation
and Drive

6

Animal Behavior and Internal Drives

CURT P. RICHTER

Psychobiological Laboratory, Phipps Psychiatric Clinic, Johns Hopkins University

The specification of drive level has been a persistent problem to the experimental psychologist interested in determining the role of drive in such psychological processes as acquisition, extinction, retention, and generalization of learned behavior. Psychologists were quick to settle on length of deprivation as the means of specifying drive in learning experiments because of its apparent objectivity and logical validity. Although hours of deprivation have been useful for specifying drive in some experiments, deficiencies of the technique render it inappropriate in other studies.

The following selection represents excerpts from an early study which points to the correlation between internal drives and activity. It is reprinted from The Quarterly Review of Biology, *1927, 2, 307-343, with the permission of the author and the publisher.*

One of the most fundamental of all the phenomena which characterize animal life and distinguish it from plant life is the spontaneous motility of the animal organism. A few plants, to be sure, especially certain forms of marine vegetation, do move about, but these few are exceptions in the plant kingdom. The activity of animals, on the other hand, although it varies widely in form and extent from species to species, is an ordinary phenomenon which one always anticipates under normal circumstances. We may ask, then, what it is that sets off the diverse performances which animals display. Ordinarily we think of most of their activity as being due to some form of external stimulation. We know, however, that all animals, from the lowest uni-cellular organism to man, are active even when all external stimuli have been eliminated. And since this spontaneous motility, just as any other kind of motility, must have a definite cause, it must be due to some natural factor within the organism. Many workers have chosen to call it "voluntary" activity, presumably because of the common belief that the "will" to do is the origin of the action. We believe, however, that spontaneous activity arises from certain underlying physiological origins. We shall attempt to show from studies chiefly on the white rat what some of these origins are, and how they fit into the general biological picture of the animal's life. . . .

PERIODIC NATURE OF SPONTANEOUS ACTIVITY—
TWO-HOUR RHYTHM

We may begin our review with the rat confined just after feeding in a small cage of the type shown in Fig. 1.

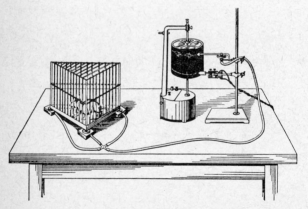

Fig. 1. Photograph of cage used in studying gross bodily activity. The cage is triangular in shape, 12 inches high and 12 inches wide. Each corner is supported on a rubber tambour through which all movements are transmitted to a recording Marey tambour. The time is recorded on the smoked paper in half hour intervals by means of an eight day clock.

The walls and floor of the cage are absolutely bare and the room in which the experiment is performed is kept constantly illuminated and free from all disquieting noises and odors. If we observe the animal for a while we see that it moves about most of the time, doing many things. It sniffs and claws at the walls of the cage, it climbs, and gnaws and scratches; but from all these observations, however interesting at first sight, we learn nothing of what makes it active. If, however, we arrange the cage so that every movement therein, even the slightest, is recorded over a period of ten to twelve hours on a smoked drum, a remarkable fact comes to light: this diffuse gross bodily activity occurs rhythmically, active periods alternating with periods of almost complete quiescence. The active periods occur at intervals varying from one to two hours. Moreover, the records show further that the activity within each active period is slight at the beginning, but increases as the period advances and reaches its maximum usually near the end (Richter, 1922). Typical records obtained from two rats in triangular cages are shown in Fig. 2. The record in Fig. 3,

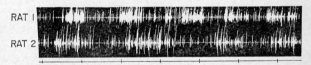

RAT 1

RAT 2

Fig. 2. Records from two adult rats showing the periodic nature of their spontaneous activity. Time is given in hours below the record.

obtained from a guinea pig in the same type of cage, is representative of a similar rhythm found in other animals.

Had the motility been irregular and non-periodic we should have accomplished nothing in our investigation of its origin. On the contrary, however, it is very significant that such well defined periods of activity, recurring at such regular intervals, are found when external conditions are as nearly constant as is practically possible. This fact would indicate that the motility rhythm must be

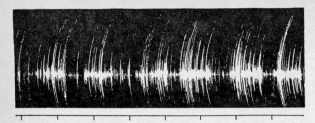

Fig. 3. Record of spontaneous activity of an adult guinea pig. Time in hours below the record.

set up from within the animal in some organ which functions at a similar frequency of one and a half to two hours.

ORIGIN OF THE TWO-HOUR-ACTIVITY RHYTHM

A review of the periodicity of the different viscera eliminates at once the heart and lungs and the sex glands, since the two former organs function at a frequency much higher and the latter at a frequency much lower than that of the bodily activity rhythm. In the stomach, however, we know that active periods alternate with quiescent intervals every hour and a half to two hours. In 1904 Boldireff was able to show that contractions occur in the walls of the empty stomach, but several years elapsed before Carlson (1916) demonstrated the periodic nature of this activity. Carlson, working with guinea pigs, dogs, and monkeys, found that from one to two hours after a meal, when the stomach is nearly empty, contraction waves begin passing downward over the stomach walls. These waves, small at first, gradually become larger and larger until they finally involve the whole lower half of the organ, and the gastric musculature often passes into a condition of semi-tetanus. Then, quite suddenly, the contractions cease and an inactive interval of an hour or more ensues. After this period of quiescence the small waves begin again, and the entire process is repeated. Thus one period follows another as long as the stomach remains empty.

Gastric movements in both animals and man have

been studied by means of the apparatus shown in Fig. 4 (Martin and Rogers, 1927). A balloon attached to the end of a tube is passed through the oesophagus into the stomach and inflated, and a manometer is fastened to

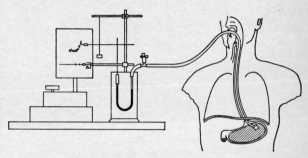

Fig. 4. *Diagram showing the method of recording the hunger contractions of the empty stomach (Martin and Rogers, 1927).*

the other end of the tube. The contractions of the stomach change the pressure on the balloon, so that some of the air is pushed up into the tube, and the level of the water in the manometer is changed. As the water rises and falls with the contraction waves, the movement is recorded by a floating pointer on a smoked drum. A record obtained by this method with similar apparatus is shown in Fig. 5. The record was taken in this laboratory

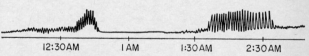

| 12:30AM | I AM | 1:30AM | 2:30AM |

Fig. 5. *Record of stomach contractions of a human adult taken during an uninterrupted sleep.*

on a human adult during a night of normal sleep. The portion presented—that portion registered between 12.30 and 2.30, when the last meal had certainly been assimilated—illustrates very clearly the cyclic nature of the movements of the empty stomach.

According to the recent observations of Rogers and Martin (1926), the stomach takes the shape shown in Fig. 6 A at the height of each of the single contractions near the end of the active period and that shown in Fig. 6 B when it is inactive and relaxed. With each of

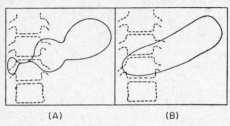

(A)   (B)

Fig. 6. A. Shape of the stomach at the height of a contraction wave. B. Shape of the relaxed stomach (Roentgenographic observations by Rogers and Martin, 1926).

these large waves, then, we see that the lower part of the stomach contracts to such an extent that the lumen practically disappears, whereas the upper part may show a contraction wave near the middle.

Cannon and Washburn (1912) and Cannon (1915) have shown that with these large contractions the sensation of hunger arises, and from the work of Rogers and Martin we know that these "hunger" contractions are set up in the lower third of the stomach. The hunger sensation is not produced until the end of the active period is nearly reached, when the waves have become very large, but even then it increases in intensity to some extent with the magnitude of the contraction, and it disappears entirely when the contractions cease. The inference, therefore, is quite logical that the two-hour periods of gross bodily activity in the rat are associated with periods of gastric movement and have to do with the hunger responses of the animal.

CORRELATION BETWEEN THE TWO-HOUR ACTIVITY RHYTHM AND THE HUNGER RESPONSE

In order to test this hypothesis we recorded simultaneously the bodily activity of the animal and the intervals at which it sought food and ate. This experiment was performed in the type of cage shown in Fig. 7. The larger compartment was simply the usual triangular activity cage shown in Fig. 1; the smaller compartment contained a cup filled with a powdered food mixture (McCollum

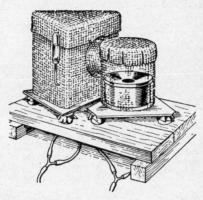

Fig. 7. Combined food and activity cage. The two compartments are supported on separate sets of tambours so that the activity in each is recorded separately.

diet). The corners of each cage were supported on rubber tambours and so arranged that the activity in the two cages was recorded separately. In this way the curve in Fig. 8 was obtained, where the activity in the large cage is registered on the first line, and that in the food-box on the second, with the time in hours below. It will be seen immediately that the animal always enters the feed-

Fig. 8. Record showing the relation between gross bodily activity and feeding periods. Activity in the large cage is given on the upper line, and entrances into the food-box on the lower. Time in hours is indicated below the record.

ing-cage and eats once during each activity period, that it enters usually near the end of the period and rarely at the beginning, and that it does not enter during a quiescent interval. Moreover, we have found through prolonged personal observation, that an adult animal rarely approaches the food-box *except to eat*, and that the vibrations recorded in the activity cage for a short time after it leaves the food-box are produced almost entirely by an extensive cleansing performance which always follows feeding. In these experiments the activity periods, recurring invariably with the entrance into the food-box, are even more regular than they were in the earlier work when no food was available. With this greater regularity, the quiescent intervals are much longer, so that the lapse between periods is three to four hours instead of one to two, as found in the activity cage with no food-box attached. The significance of the lengthened intervals will be discussed below.

We may now attempt to show in more detail how the gross bodily activity, the feeding habits, and the stomach contractions seem to be correlated. The simultaneous records of activity and feeding suggest that a close relationship must exist between the periods observed in the simple activity cage and the hunger "drive" of the animal. From the experimental data compiled above we know that the motility rhythm and the stomach contraction rhythm have three features in common: the frequency of both varies between one and two hours; the active phases of both begin at slight intensity and increase gradually, reaching a maximum near the end; and in both the active period ends abruptly and is followed by a quiescent interval. If we represent the two rhythms as in Fig. 9 A, drawing a diagrammatic activity record directly above a diagrammatic record of gastric movement, so that the active phases of the two coincide, we find that the small stomach contractions occur simultaneously with the beginning of the motility period, and that as the magnitude of the contractions increases the animal becomes more and more active. But how can we justify our representation in terms of the hunger response? It is very probable that as long as the animal experiences the hunger sensation which accompanies the stomach movements, it seeks for food, unsuccessfully, of course, in the single cage without a food-box. When the gastric contractions stop, however, the hunger disappears and the animal becomes quiet again.

On this basis one might expect that when food was available all the time, the rat would enter the food-box as soon as the contractions began. Actually, however, we know that it moves about in the main cage for some time before it approaches the food-box. How, then, can we explain this preliminary diffuse activity? Here again, as in Fig. 9 A, the relationship may be represented sche-

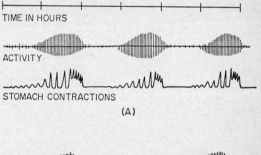

(A)

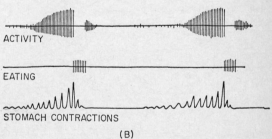

(B)

Fig. 9. Schematic representation of the relation between periods of gross bodily activity and stomach contractions. A. Simple activity cage without food. B. Double cage with food.

matically. In Fig. 9 B, a record taken simultaneously from the activity cage and the food-box is shown in diagram on the first and second lines, and a stomach contraction record on the third. Thus we see that the small contractions give rise to the diffuse activity in the large cage. The animal seems at first simply to be annoyed and becomes more and more restless as the contractions grow larger, until the "main" contractions set in and the general discomfort becomes centralized in the hunger sensation. This stimulus dominates the behavior of the organism and it enters the food-box to eat. When its appetite has been satisfied, it passes into a period of quiescence which lasts until the stomach has become empty and the contractions have started up again. And since time is required for the contents of the stomach to be digested, the interval between contraction periods is three to four hours instead of one to two hours as observed in the earlier experiments. . . .

FEEDING HABITS OF THE RAT

Starting from our observations on the relation between activity and the feeding periods of the rat, we decided to extend our investigation to a study of its food habits, with special reference to their regularity. For this purpose cages shown in Fig. 12 were constructed. They consisted of individual compartments large enough for the animals

Fig. 12. Cages used for studying food-habits.

to take plenty of exercise, with a small tunnel on one side at the top leading to the food-box. This tunnel was built in an inconvenient position in order to discourage the rat as much as possible from entering it except when driven by hunger. The food-cup was placed at the end of the tunnel under the wire cloth floor, and a hole was made in the floor just large enough for the rat to insert its head. Whenever it reached in for food, the balance of the cup on a large tambour was disturbed and a mark was made on a smoked drum.

The records obtained in these cages bring out clearly the great constancy of the feeding habits of the rat. The record in Fig. 13, taken on an adult animal from 8 p.m.

Fig. 13. Record showing the feeding periods of an adult rat. Time is registered at half-hour intervals.

to 8 a.m., shows that the feeding period recurred about once every three hours throughout the day, and when the experiments were extended over a longer time, it was found that the rhythm persisted very constantly from day to day (see Fig. 14). Similar experiments on other animals confirmed these results. A rat may eat seven times a day or it may eat eight or ten times, but in any case it maintains a constant average from one day to the next.

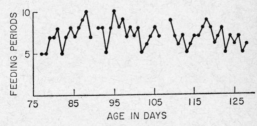

Fig. 14. Graph showing the regularity of the feeding periods of an adult rat from day to day. The number of periods per day is given on the ordinates and the age of the animal in days on the abscissae.

The degree of variability of the feeding response is shown very clearly by the curve in Fig. 15, compiled from records taken on four animals for twenty successive days. The abscissae represent the length of the intervals recorded

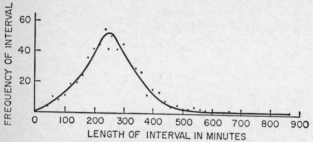

Fig. 15. Frequency curve of intervals of various lengths between feeding periods in four adult male rats for twenty days.

between feedings, and the ordinates indicate the number of times each interval was recorded from any one of the four individuals. The curve is evenly balanced with a mode of two hundred and fifty minutes, or approximately four hours. The few longer intervals, we believe, may be identified entirely with periods during which the rat, like the human being, slept in spite of the stomach contractions.

From the above experiments it seems fairly well established, then, that the hunger contractions stimulate the organism to activity, but what the details of the mechanism are we are not prepared to discuss. We do believe, however, that somehow, with each new hunger contraction period, impulses are sent up the afferent nerves from the stomach to the brain and out to the striped muscles, to release the energy stored up there. . . .

REFERENCES

CANNON, W. B. 1915. Bodily Changes in Pain, Hunger, Fear, and Rage; an Account of Recent Researches into the Function of Emotional Excitement. New York.

———— and WASHBURN, A. L. 1912. An explanation of hunger. Amer. J. of Physiol., 29, p. 441.

CARLSON, A. J. 1916. The Control of Hunger in Health and Disease. Chicago.

MARTIN, C. L., and ROGERS, F. T. 1927. Hunger pain. Amer. J. of Roentgenology and Radium Therapy, 17, no. 2, p. 222.

RICHTER, C. P: 1922. A behavioristic study of the activity of the rat. Comp. Psychology Monographs, 1, no. 2.

ROGERS, F. T., and MARTIN, C. L. 1926. X-ray observations of hunger contractions in man. Amer. J. of Physiol., 76, p. 349.

7

Standard Apparatus for the Study of Animal Motivation[1]

T. N. JENKINS, L. H. WARNER,
AND C. J. WARDEN
Columbia University

The following passages describe an objective and quantitative measure of drive strength. The obstruction method which is described rests on the assumption that the strength of a drive such as hunger, thirst, or sex can be measured by determining the number of times an animal will overcome a barrier to achieve a goal or obtain an object—food, water, or an animal of the opposite sex. The method is of considerable value because it has formed the historical basis for more refined techniques for drive assessment. One recently developed method is the quinine suppression technique in which food or water is adulterated with a bitter tasting substance. The degree to which eating or drinking behavior is suppressed serves as an index of drive. That is, a hungry or thirsty animal will accept a more bitter taste in food or water than will an animal that is not deprived.

These excerpts are reprinted from The Journal of Comparative Psychology, 1926, 6, 361-382, *with the permission of the authors and The Williams & Wilkins Co.*

. . . In the first section of the present report a description is given of an apparatus for the measurement of drives by the Method of Obstruction. The apparatus has been developed during the past two years in the Columbia laboratory in connection with a research project

[1] This apparatus was constructed in connection with a research project on animal drives supported by the Council for Research in the Social Sciences of Columbia University.

on motivation in the white rat. It can be readily adapted, however, to most common mammalian forms, and thus offers possibilities in comparative studies within this field. Great pains have been taken to standardize the essential features by the use of automatic devices when possible and by exactitude of detail in construction. The control procedure as developed will also be indicated.

The second section is a description of an improved apparatus of the choice method type, following the general pattern used by Tsai.[2] The improvement consists, in the main, in the introduction of automatic electrical devices permitting a more adequate control of the animal and of the incentive stimuli. Standard problems and procedure are suggested.

I. THE OBSTRUCTION METHOD APPARATUS

As previously stated, this method involves the placing of an obstruction of some sort between the organism and the incentive stimulus. In order to obtain the latter and satisfy the dominant demand of the moment, the organism is required to surmount the obstruction. In the present apparatus the obstruction employed is an electric grill supplied with a constant current of quantitatively determined attributes. Various other types of obstruction might be used but the electric stimulation has the advantage of being more convenient to control and administer than most others would be. For the sake of clarity in description the obstruction apparatus will be divided into two parts and each treated in order. First, the box for the control of the animal and the administering of the shock; and second, the device for the control of the electrical current supplied to the box in the obstruction section, permitting definite systematic variation of the same. This description of the apparatus will be followed by a discussion of methods of controlling the intra-organic state of the organism for this type of investigation, kinds of data that may be obtained by this general method, and standard problems to which the method offers an experimental approach.

[2] Tsai, Chiao: The relative strength of sex and hunger motives in the albino rat. *Jour. Comp. Psych.*, 1925, v, 407.

1. the animal control box

The ground plan of this part of the apparatus is shown in Fig. 1. The box consists essentially of three compartments as follows: entrance compartment A, obstruction compartment, B, and incentive compartment, C-D, di-

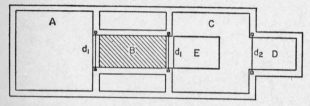

Fig. 1. Diagram of floor plan of the obstruction box. A, entrance compartment; B, obstruction compartment; C, D, divided incentive compartment; E, release plate; d_1, manually operated door of entrance compartment; d_2, automatic door (operated by release plate) between two divisions of incentive compartment.

vided into two sections for reasons indicated later. The body of the box is built of whitewood and is finished both without and within in dull black. It rests upon a table 30 inches in height which also serves to support the elaborate electrical equipment necessary to furnish the shock to the grill in compartment B.

The entrance compartment A is 10 inches square and 10 inches deep, inside measurements. It is entirely separated from compartment B by a wooden partition except for a doorway 4 inches square leading into the tunnel that crosses the latter compartment. This doorway is fitted with a door of thin sheet steel, d_1, which slides in felt-lined grooves, and is therefore practically noiseless. It is operated by hand by means of a cord which passes through a bent glass tube (instead of the usual pulley device) to a point outside the box, so that its operation cannot be observed by the animal in the compartment. In closing, the door sinks into a narrow felt-lined groove in the floor. The purpose of the door is obviously to re-

strain the animal in the entrance compartment until
such time as the experimenter may wish to test its reaction to the obstruction-incentive situation beyond. The
compartment is covered by a panel of heavy plate glass,
but may be opened by sliding the panel, which rests in
a felt-lined groove, back over compartment B.

The dimensions of compartment B are exactly the
same as those above enumerated for compartment A, except for the fact that the effective part of the compartment is restricted to a tunnel 4 inches wide and 4 inches
high connecting the entrance and incentive compartments. The entire floor of compartment B consists of an
electric grill set in the wooden base of the box so that
it comes up even with the floor of the two adjacent compartments. The conducting elements in the grill are number 18 copper wires wound upon a slab of bakelite ½
inch thick. The turns are ¼ inch apart, and are wound
in such a way that the turns from the two terminals of
the transformer alternate. A rat in crossing the grill will
close the circuit, therefore, by stepping upon any two
consecutive turns. This practically insures stimulation
from the instant the animal steps upon the grill. Moss
used, as a shocking device, two plates placed some distance apart along a passageway, simultaneous contact
with both plates being necessary to produce the shock.
The grill above described offers a much more dependable
and uniform source of stimulation.

The presentation of the electrical stimulation to the
animal offers certain difficulties. After trying out several
other schemes the tunnel device was finally selected as
being the most satisfactory. At first it was thought desirable to place the grill in the center of the box without
any further separation into definite compartments. This
would allow the animal to make contact at any point
along the edge of the grill, and to have free passage from
A to C across any portion of it. This arrangement was
found to be unsatisfactory. Many of the animals would
attempt, and sometimes with success, to jump from A
to C, a distance of 10 inches, without touching the grill.
To prevent this two pieces of plate glass, extending 6
inches from either wall at a point 3 inches from the
edges of the grill, were so placed that the animal must

pass through a winding pathway approximately 4 inches wide in crossing the grill. This arrangement eliminated the jumping behavior quite successfully and also aided in marking off the obstruction part of the box from the entrance part.

However, a further difficulty arose which led us to separate the box into 3 definite compartments, as above described, by partitions, and to install the tunnel device. It became clear from observing the behavior of the animals, especially when a high degree of shock was used, that they did not discriminate readily between the entrance and obstruction portions of the box when not so divided. Usually they would rush pell mell across the grill to the incentive portion of the box the instant they were placed at A, and after rushing to C paid no heed whatsoever to the incentive stimulus (food), but attempted to escape by jumping up against the glass panel covering the box or, perhaps crouched sullenly in a corner. Rats that had been starved for long periods of time (one to three days) responded in this manner. The animals seemed to be dominated by fear of the combined A-B situation rather than by hunger. They were apparently avoiding the entrance and obstruction sections rather than seeking the incentive section. This escape response would be reënacted promptly, over and over again, as soon as the animal was returned to the entrance end of the box, in preparation for a succeeding test.

When A and B were separated into compartments by partitions, and the animal restrained in compartment A by the door, d_1, for a brief interval of time between successive tests, no such behavior occurred. This suggests that the animal probably did not discriminate, in the former arrangement, between the entrance and obstruction portions of the box. A-B as a whole rather than just B was avoided, since the two portions were not sufficiently isolated to be readily discriminated as separate sources of stimuli which might serve as the basis of a differential response. The copper wires on the B portion of the floor constituted the only important difference between that and the A portion, and the line of junction between the two was not very marked since the grill had been made to fit very neatly into the floor of the box.

A second possible explanation for this escape behavior can be made in terms of a conditioning process of the substitute stimulus type as indicated in the following diagram:

S (shock at B)_____R (escape into C)

S (sight of B while still in A)

This explanation assumes that the A portion of the box had been actually discriminated from the B portion at first, but later came to serve essentially as a single situation, by virtue of the substitution indicated above. At any rate the separating of the box into definite compartments, as in the present apparatus, together with the introduction of a brief interval of time between successive tests remedied the difficulty.

The tunnel across the grill is 4 inches wide, 4 inches high and 10 inches long. The two sides are of wood, and the top of plate glass to permit the same degree of illumination in this as in the other two compartments of the box. The use of the tunnel has the effect of making the response to the obstruction more definite, since there is only this single point of approach and contact. Accidental contacts with the grill are now much less likely to occur than under the old arrangement. Furthermore, the movements of different animals in passing over the grill are more uniform—they must either walk or run. This makes possible relative constancy in the amount of electrical stimulation involved in the act of crossing, this latter being the chief unit of measurement on the behavior side.

The incentive section includes a double compartment, C-D, as indicated in the diagram. The division into two parts would not be necessary with such incentives as different kinds of food, or other non-living stimuli. However, when the incentive stimulus is a living animal (such as a female in testing the male sex drive) it is usually necessary to confine the stimulus animal in order to prevent it from crossing over to the test animal. The method of restraining the stimulus animal should be as natural as possible so as not to arouse in it behavior likely to reduce its efficacy as a normal positive stimulus. The restraint should cease at the moment the test animal has completed the act of crossing the grill, and the release of the stimulus animal should be automatic, if possible.

Moss restrained the female rat in the incentive chamber by a simple door that must be raised by the experimenter, presumably as the animal was crossing the grill. Such a method involves the error of inexact timing —of opening the door either too soon or too late. Furthermore, the moving door might be a factor of central importance in the stimulation situation during the test. A door of ordinary opaque material would decrease the visual, and probably the olfactory stimulation in connection with the animal in the incentive chamber. The movement of the door would likely serve also as a distraction to the test animal.

We have endeavored to avoid all these difficulties by the use of a separate restraining chamber, D, the entrance to which is guarded by the translucent door, d_2 (Figs. 1 and 2) which is opened automatically by the test animal in the act of crossing the grill. The door is 4 inches square, constructed of celluloid $\frac{1}{8}$ inch in thickness and is therefore semi-transparent. Three small windows, each 1 inch square, cut in the upper half of the door, permit the free passage of olfactory stimuli, whether of food or of sex object, from the restraint chamber.

The mechanism of the automatic door release is illustrated in Fig. 2. An opening 4 inches wide and 6 inches long is cut in the floor of compartment C directly in front of the exit of the tunnel. In this opening the release plate, E, is set flush with the floor. The plate is of wood and painted a dull black so as to be distinguished with difficulty from the adjacent floor. It is supported by a hinge, F, and the adjustable coil spring, G. Fastened rigidly to the lower surface of the release plate is the L-shaped rod, H, at the tip of which is the silver contact point, I. The tension of the spring, G, is just sufficient to keep this point in contact with the small silver plate, J. This latter is mounted on the rod, K, which is adjustable in the vertical plane, being pivoted at the wooden block, L. The V-shaped wooden block, M, spans the rod,

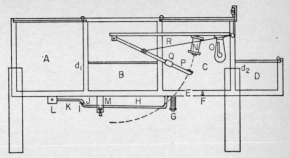

Fig. 2. Diagram of side elevation of the obstruction box.
A, entrance compartment; B, obstruction compartment; C, D,
divided incentive compartment; E, release plate; d_1, manually
operated door of entrance compartment; d_2, automatic door
(operated by release plate) between two divisions of incentive
compartment; F, a hinge and G, an adjustable coil spring,
both supporting the release plate; H, a rod rigidly secured to
the release plate; I and J, silver contacts; K, a rod pivoted at L,
the adjustment of which determines the level of the release
plate when the latter is not depressed; M, a block carrying
the bolt adjusting the depth of depression of the release plate;
N, electro-magnet supporting free end of the pendulum, P, prior
to its release; O, in circuit with the magnet and acting as resistance and as a signal; Q, adjustable pendulum weight; R,
cord conveying movement of pendulum to the door, d_2.

H, and in the base of this block is a rubber pad which
can be raised or lowered by an adjustable nut. The rod,
H, rests on this pad when the release plate is fully depressed.

In circuit with the points I and J, is an electro-magnet,
N, of 1200 ohms resistance, and a 10-watt electric lamp,
O, both of which are mounted on the underside of a
15-inch shelf fastened on the outside of the box. Suspended from cone bearings at the other end of the shelf
is a pendulum, P, made of ¼ inch square brass tubing
which carries an adjustable weight consisting of a brass
collar held in place by a set screw. A small piece of iron
is soldered to the pendulum at such a point that when
the latter is raised the iron will make contact with the
pole of the magnet, N, and be held in contact if the

current is passing through the magnet. A piece of felt fastened over the pole of the magnet serves to deaden the click produced by this contact. By means of a cord and 3 small pulleys, the falling pendulum lifts the door, d_2. Any tendency to rebound is entirely overcome by the friction within the system.

The operation of this automatic door release is exceedingly simple and practically noiseless. At the first touch of the release plate by the animal in crossing the grill, the contact between I and J is broken, to be re-made only after the animal has entirely cleared the plate. The maximum depth of depression of the release plate is controlled by the device at M and need not be more than 2 or 3 mm., the rod, K, being always adjusted so that the plate is flush with the floor of the compartment. The tension of the spring, G, can be easily and quickly adjusted for animals of any weight. We have found that a tension of 40 grams is sufficiently delicate when 80-gram rats are being tested.

Even when the white rat dashes through the tunnel at high speed, the action of the automatic door release is so prompt that the animal never comes into collision with the rising door. Indeed the door does not seem to be noticed by the animal at all. The stimulus animal is visible in the restraint chamber through the windows of the celluloid door even when the latter is closed. The restraint chamber is 4 by 4 by 6 inches in size and is covered with plate glass. It can be removed by the simple turning of a thumbscrew for purposes of cleansing or deodorizing. All incentive stimuli, whether living animals or food, etc., are placed in the restraint chamber, so that the automatic door device is utilized in testing the strength of any drive.

The obstruction apparatus is placed for use in a dark room in which the only source of light is an illumination hood. This latter is made of wood and is 36 inches long and 4 inches wide and deep. It is heavily coated with flat white inside so as to make a good reflecting surface, and finished on the outer surface in dull black. The hood extends the full length of the control box at a point approximately 12 inches above the box in the central position. It is illuminated by 8 lights of 3 C.P., set at equal intervals (4 inches) along the top of the hood within. The light is diffused through a sheet of translucent paper lying above the "Celotex" screen that covers the lower open side of the hood facing the box. A piece of ground glass of the proper grade would likely do as well. The hood device gives a uniform illumination of the interior of all compartments of the box, the outside environment being, at the same time, relatively unilluminated. This arrangement permits the experimenter to observe the behavior of the animal freely during the test period, while remaining practically invisible to the animal. . . .

8

A Study of Hunger Behavior in the White Rat by Means of the Obstruction Method [1]

L. H. WARNER

Columbia University

The following selection demonstrates the application of the obstruction method to the study of the relation of hunger drive to increasing periods of food deprivation. The results obtained by Warner contribute to the belief that hunger drive level increases with increasing food deprivation intervals.

The selection is reprinted from The Journal of Comparative Psychology, 1928, 8, 273-299, *with the permission of the author and* The Williams & Wilkins Co.

In a recent monograph (10) were published the results of an experimental study of sex behavior in male and female white rats. The method used in that study has been termed the obstruction method (3). The most important data consist of the records of the number of times in a test period of constant duration that an animal will cross an electric grid to reach a sex object (an animal of the opposite sex). The effect upon this tendency to approach a sex object or, in brief, the effect upon the sex drive of variation in physiological condition was studied. In the female it was found that the sex drive was dominant during only a rather restricted phase of the entire oestrous cycle, that during this period (the cornified stage) the crossing was decidedly and reliably more

[1] This report covers one major topic in a project on animal drives under the general direction of Prof. C. J. Warden, supported by the Council for Research in the Social Sciences of Columbia University.

frequent than during the dioestrous stages. The average number of crossings per unit time made by the animals tested when in the cornified stage, at the peak of sex activity, can be considered an index of the sex drive in the normal female.

In the case of the male the factor influencing most profoundly the sex drive is the length of time which has elapsed since the last previous mating period. Of the seven sex deprivation intervals studied the twenty-four hour interval resulted in the maximum drive. The results for this group may be considered an index of the sex drive in the normal male.

A second fundamental type of behavior to be studied is that directed toward food. Such behavior has previously been studied by Moss (4) and by Holden (2) using the obstruction method. The results of neither of these investigations can be compared with those of the sex study mentioned above because of decided dissimilarities in method. These will be enumerated in a later section.

The present article is a report of the experimental study of food-seeking behavior made under such conditions as to render the results directly comparable with those presented in the monograph on sex behavior. It also includes a comparison of these results with those on the sex drive.

METHODS AND PROCEDURE

The animals used were of the same stock and raised under the same conditions in every particular as were those used in the study of sex behavior. The apparatus and general procedure were the same. There will be taken up here consideration of only such matters as refer especially to feeding conditions. For further details see Warner (10).

The animals had from the time of weaning been supplied with a diet which was adequate qualitatively and quantitatively. The details of the diet during their first hundred and fifty days during which they were in the care of the Wistar Institute cannot be given, but the long and successful experience of this organization in the care and breeding of normal animals is ample guarantee of its adequacy. During the thirty-five days each animal was in this laboratory prior to testing the following diet was supplied it continuously:

	Per cent
Whole wheat flour	70.0
Whole milk powder	16.6
Casein	11.0
Sodium chloride	1.4
Calcium carbonate	1.0

This was mixed, dry, in an electric mixer for at least ten minutes. Greens were supplied in abundance once a week. There was always an ample supply of water from inverted bottles which rendered fouling impossible. More than a sufficient supply of food was kept in the cages at all times (except, of course, during the starvation periods mentioned below). These feeding conditions differed in no way from those which held in the study of the sex drive but are described here since they are closely related to the hunger drive here under investigation.

Just as in the study of sex behavior the physiological condition of the animal as related to food consumption was kept as constant as possible (and in that condition accompanying a minimum of food-seeking activity), so in this study we have determined and kept constant the animal's condition as this related to sex behavior and have used those conditions accompanying a minimum amount of sex behavior. In no other investigation of either of these types of behavior has such control been attempted or, perhaps, even the need for it recognized. This criticism holds for even the more recent work (Simmons (7), Moss (4), Tsai (9), Holden (2)).

The most dominant factors affecting sex activity in the female are, apparently, (1) the present stimulus situation and (2) the oestrous condition. To take up the first of these factors: there was no element in the experimental situation which seemed at all related to, and thus likely to arouse sex behavior. Although it seems well nigh impossible to control the olfactory situation when animals of the two sexes are used on the same apparatus we at least spared no effort in attempting to do so. Animals of the opposite sex were not used in the apparatus on the same night (all experimentation took place between 9 P.M. and 4 A.M., as in the case of the sex study).

Immediately at the conclusion of a period of experimentation the apparatus was thoroughly washed out with soap solution and allowed to air. At no time was an animal given the opportunity of associating the apparatus with another animal. In other words, but one animal at a time was in the apparatus, the object in the incentive compartment being not another animal but food. The second factor was controlled by determining the oestrous condition of the animal at the time of its testing. This determination was based upon the histological characteristics of the vaginal secretion. Sampling of the secretion was never made until after the animal had been tested; thus there was eliminated the possibility that this process might interfere with the normal behavior of the animal during testing. Sex activity in the female is rather rigidly restricted to a relatively brief portion of the oestrous cycle. During the remainder of the cycle the animal rarely shows any interest in the male as a sex object and will, in fact, actively avoid mating in most cases. By using females in the inactive period or dioestrum the sex factor is reduced to the minimum. The data reported herein concern only such females as were in the following stages as defined in the study on sex behavior: Recuperative, Early inactive, Inactive and Late inactive. Several females were in oestrum at the time of testing (as determined afterward by smear examination) in spite of the fact that the females were selected for testing on the basis of behavior observation which seemed to indicate that they were in dioestrum. Data on such animals were discarded. There was not a sufficient number of them to make it worth while to consider them as a separate group.

The dominant factors affecting sex behavior in the male are (1) the present stimulus situation and (2) the period of time which has elapsed since the last previous mating period. The first of these was controlled as in the case of the female. The second was kept constant in the case of all males used. The sex deprivation interval immediately preceding testing was thirty-five days. This long period was determined upon after careful consideration of the results of the study on the sex drive. When studying food-seeking behavior it was not merely our purpose to keep conditions affecting the sex drive constant but so to arrange them that the sex drive should be at its minimum at the time of the testing. This cannot be done as simply with the male as in the case of the female since the male is not subject to a cycle involving a period of sex inactivity. It might be suggested that we use males immediately after they had been given a period of mating, after sex "satiation" had resulted. While it is true that the sex drive appears to be at its minimum at this time our observations upon rats tested (in the obstruction apparatus with a female in oestrum in the incentive compartment) when in this condition indicate that their behavior is so profoundly affected that a fair measure of the food-seeking drive could not be obtained. Such males were found to be extremely inactive. The usual type of behavior displayed was sleep (or what appeared to be such).

Again it might be suggested that we use males whose sex drive had been partially satiated. But casual laboratory observations appear to indicate that the drive remains at a high point under this condition although it is displayed rather more spasmodically.

Nor would the use of males after a short deprivation interval prove satisfactory. As has been shown in the sex study, recovery of the sex drive is very rapid. It is apparently well along the road to recovery by the time (varying with different animals) when the male becomes aroused from the lethargy following a prolonged period of mating. It thus seems that if we should use a rather short sex deprivation interval we would not be dealing with a homogeneous group of animals but with a group containing both lethargic and active animals.

A sex deprivation period of one day has been shown to result in sex behavior at or near the high point. But a glance at Fig. 4 in the sex monograph shows that beyond this point there is a gradual drop in the drive. The longest sex deprivation interval used in that study was one of twenty-eight days. A decided falling off in the strength of the drive was found in this group of twenty

males. Just as significant for
consideration of the behavior
eight day sex-deprived animal   placed i
tion involving sex stimulation.   tne twenty ni
tested only two crossed to the female during the fi
minute. This is the lowest number recorded for any
group, being even lower than that for the control group
(no sex object or other incentive). This indicates that
these two crossings were very probably determined by
other stimulation than that related to sex. During the
first five minutes but sixteen crossings were recorded for
the twenty-eight day group as contrasted with seventy-
six for the one day group. After the first five minutes
the activity became progressively greater indicating what
might be described as a reawakening of interest in the
sex object.

As has been pointed out in the sex study, the sex drive
in the male appears to be more determined by the external stimulation and less by the internal stimulation
than in the case of the female. Thus sufficiently long
deprivation periods in the male produce a drop in the
drive such as would be much less true of the female because of the rhythmic occurrence of an internal stimulus
situation in the latter. It is true that the male after a
long period of sex deprivation can recover in a few minutes its normal interest in a sex object when it is placed
in the presence of a female in oestrum. This fact does
not, however, prevent such males from being the ideal
animals for our present purpose since there is nothing in
the situation involved in the measurement of the hunger drive which would directly, or by association arouse
the sex drive.

Thus by using long time (35-day) sex deprived males
in the present study of the hunger drive we feel that we
are keeping constant and at a minimum the sex drive.
These animals may in fact be considered somewhat analogous to females in dioestrum.

The incentive stimulus in the present study was food,
about twenty grams of the mixture described above. This
food was contained in a black metal receptacle firmly
fixed in the smaller section of the incentive compartment, i.e., where the incentive or stimulus animal was

study of the sex drive. (See either of the
references for cuts and description of the ap-
...ed: (3) or (10)). The automatic door, which
... its purpose the restraint of the incentive animal
...the study of sex, operated in just the way it did in
that study although it was of course not necessary to
restrain the food. In brief, except for the fact that a
food object was substituted for a sex object the experimental conditions were no different from those which
held in the study of the sex drive.

The behavior which determined when the animal
should be returned to the entrance compartment after
crossing consisted in the taking of a nibble of food. This
criterion was adhered to with the following exceptions.
If during the preliminary training period the animal did
not take one nibble of food within one minute it was returned anyway. This period was reduced to thirty seconds
during the test period. This exception had a particular
bearing on the groups of animals which were run immediately after being taken from cages containing food, i.e.,
after no starvation period. These animals, as would be
expected, failed to respond to the food any more than
to other details of the incentive compartment. As a matter of fact, crossing was far less frequent in animals of
this group even though they were sometimes returned
prior to sampling the food.

It was originally planned that a control group corresponding to that group showing the greatest hunger drive
should be tested. This group was to have differed from
the test group only in that there would be no food or
other incentive object in the incentive compartment
while the animals were tested. Our results showed, however, such reliable differences between the behavior of
animals recently fed and those starved for a period that
it was felt that additional indication that the differential
behavior was a function of the animal's condition as
related to food was unnecessary. It might be noted paren-
thetically that the control groups run in the sex study
cannot serve as controls for this investigation in spite of
the fact that these groups consisted of animals tested
with no object in the incentive compartment. This is
true because the female control consisted of females in

oestrum (whereas the females used in the present study were in dioestrum) and the male control consisted of males taken immediately from cages supplied with food (and would thus not be comparable with the four day starvation group, which in the present study showed the hunger drive at its height in the male).

The periods of starvation first studied in this investigation were 0, 2, 4, 6 and 8 days. The 3-day group was later added as a result of data already obtained since these seemed to indicate the possibility that the peak of food-seeking activity for the two sexes combined might lie between 2 and 4 days. Standard groups of twenty animals each were used as was done in the study of the sex drive and as is being done in other studies on drive to be published from this laboratory. The grouping is tabulated in Table 1.

TABLE 1

SHOWING GROUPING OF ANIMALS AND THE NUMBER
OF EACH SEX IN GROUP

LENGTH OF STARVATION PERIOD	NUMBER OF ANIMALS	
	Male	Female
days		
0	10	10
2	10	10
3	10	10
4	10	10
6	10	10
8	10	10

RESULTS

Table 2 gives the distribution of the approaches, contacts and crossings for the various groups. The medians, ranges, averages, standard deviations, and coefficients of variability are found in Table 3. Table 4 gives the reliability of the differences between the average crossings for various groups. The approaches, contacts and crossings as distributed minute by minute throughout the twenty minute test period are given in Table 5. In Table 6 these data are combined in five-minute units and are also reduced to percentages. Figure 1 shows graphically the effect of variation in the starvation period upon the aver-

TABLE 2

DISTRIBUTION TABLE COVERING APPROACHES, CONTACTS AND CROSSINGS FOR THE VARIOUS PERIODS OF STARVATION OF MALE AND FEMALE RATS

INTERVAL	0 Appr. M	0 Appr. F	0 Cont. M	0 Cont. F	0 Cross. M	0 Cross. F	2 Appr. M	2 Appr. F	2 Cont. M	2 Cont. F	2 Cross. M	2 Cross. F	3 Appr. M	3 Appr. F	3 Cont. M	3 Cont. F	3 Cross. M	3 Cross. F	4 Appr. M	4 Appr. F	4 Cont. M	4 Cont. F	4 Cross. M	4 Cross. F	6 Appr. M	6 Appr. F	6 Cont. M	6 Cont. F	6 Cross. M	6 Cross. F	8 Appr. M	8 Appr. F	8 Cont. M	8 Cont. F	8 Cross. M	8 Cross. F
0	5	3	2	1	5	3	2	3	1	1				1	1				1	1	1				1	2	3	3			1	1	1	2	1	2
1	3	3	2	2	1	1		1	1				2						2	1	1				2		1				2		3	1		1
2		2	3	2		3	3		1																2		1				1	1		1		
3				1		1		2							1						4				1		1				1					
4			2	1		1	1			2		1	1	1	1						2	1			1	2	1	1					2		2	
5				1	1		1	1	1	2	1			1		4			1	2	2	4	1		1	1	1			2	1	1				1
6	1			1			1	1	3	1		1	2	1	2	2	1		2	2	1	3				1	1		1			1	1		1	1
7							1	2					4	1	1	1		1	2			1						2						1		2
8	1		1		1	1			1					4	2				1			1						1			2					1
9		1			1				1	1	1			1			1	1	1	1					2	1	1	1	1			3		1	3	
10		1												1		2	1	1		1						1			2	1		1	1	1		1
11							1								1														1		2	1		1		
12										1			1											1				1						1	1	
13							1		1		1				1														1	1				1	1	
14								1		1				1		1		1					1	1						1			1			
15																	1	1						1				1	1	1			1			1
16												1																		1				1		
17											1						1						2													
18										1	2	1						1						1						1						
19											1	1					1	1						1					1	1					1	

TABLE 2 (cont.)

INTERVAL	0 App. Male	0 App. Female	0 Con. Male	0 Con. Female	0 Cross. Male	0 Cross. Female	2 DAYS App. Male	2 DAYS App. Female	2 DAYS Con. Male	2 DAYS Con. Female	2 DAYS Cross. Male	2 DAYS Cross. Female	3 DAYS App. Male	3 DAYS App. Female	3 DAYS Con. Male	3 DAYS Con. Female	3 DAYS Cross. Male	3 DAYS Cross. Female	4 DAYS App. Male	4 DAYS App. Female	4 DAYS Con. Male	4 DAYS Con. Female	4 DAYS Cross. Male	4 DAYS Cross. Female	6 DAYS App. Male	6 DAYS App. Female	6 DAYS Con. Male	6 DAYS Con. Female	6 DAYS Cross. Male	6 DAYS Cross. Female	8 DAYS App. Male	8 DAYS App. Female	8 DAYS Con. Male	8 DAYS Con. Female	8 DAYS Cross. Male	8 DAYS Cross. Female
20												1					2			1				1												
21											1							1		1			1													
22																							1						1							
23											1												1	1												
24											1	1						1					1						1	1						
25																								1						1						
26																																				
27												1																								
28												2					1						1													
29																	1																			
30																																				
31																																				
32																																				
33																																				
34																																				
35																																				
36																		1																		

TABLE 3

...ING RESULTS FOR EACH STARVATION PERIOD

STARVATION PERIOD	SEX	APPROACHES					CONTACTS					CROSSINGS				
		Median	Range	Average	Standard deviation	Coefficient of variability	Median	Range	Average	Standard deviation	Coefficient of variability	Median	Range	Average	Standard deviation	Coefficient of variability
days																
0	Female	1	0-7	2.0	1.34	67	2	0-6	3.5	1.55	44	2	0-7	2.1	2.07	98
	Male	0	0-7	1.5	1.34	89	2	0-6	2.2	1.20	55	1.5	0-9	2.7	3.37	125
	Total	1	0-7	1.75	1.36	79	2	0-6	2.85	1.42	50	2	0-9	2.4	2.78	116
2	Female	3	0-6	3.4	1.56	46	5	0-15	6.9	1.87	27	18	3-29	19.0	8.91	47
	Male	2	0-9	3.3	1.47	44	5	0-12	4.9	1.59	32	18	3-25	16.1	6.56	41
	Total	3	0-9	3.35	2.81	84	5	0-15	5.9	3.92	66	18	3-29	17.6	7.78	44
3	Female	6	1-8	5.2	1.25	24	7	6-14	8.0	1.41	76	16	9-36	18.4	7.63	41
	Male	5	1-11	5.0	1.41	.28	5	0-10	5.7	1.58	28	17	7-30	18.0	7.52	42
	Total	6	1-11	5.1	2.46	48	6	0-14	6.85	2.93	43	17	7-36	18.2	7.58	42
4	Female	5	2-9	5.2	2.04	39	6	4-8	5.7	1.10	19	18	4-26	17.0	5.92	35
	Male	4	0-7	3.6	2.20	61	3	1-5	2.8	1.17	42	19	10-29	19.1	5.87	31
	Total	5	0-9	4.4	2.37	54	5	1-8	4.75	1.91	40	18	4-29	18.1	5.98	33
6	Female	5	1-12	6.1	1.77	29	6	0-13	5.3	1.80	34	13	4-27	14.0	7.18	51
	Male	2	0-9	3.6	1.59	44	2	0-9	3.0	1.55	52	12	3-25	14.2	5.98	42
	Total	4	1-12	4.85	3.58	74	3	0-13	4.15	3.61	87	13	3-27	14.1	6.61	47
8	Female	8	0-12	6.8	1.69	25	8	0-16	7.3	2.29	31	6	0-16	6.0	4.69	78
	Male	3	0-10	4.6	1.79	39	4	0-16	5.5	2.18	40	11	0-19	9.8	5.33	54
	Total	7	0-12	5.7	3.77	66	4	0-16	6.4	5.71	89	7	0-19	7.9	5.07	64

TABLE 4

SHOWING RELIABILITY OF THE DIFFERENCES BETWEEN THE AVERAGE CROSSINGS OF EACH GROUP

GROUPS	STANDARD DEVIATION OF THE DIFFERENCE	DIFFERENCE BETWEEN THE AVERAGES	DIFFERENCE S. D. OF DIFFERENCE	CHANCES IN 100 OF A TRUE DIFFERENCE
0 and 2 days	2.43	15.1	6.21	100
2 days and 3 days	2.36	.7	.3	62
3 days and 4 days	2.17	.1	.05	52
4 days and 6 days	2.00	4.0	2.0	98
6 days and 8 days	1.86	6.2	3.33	100
0 and 3 days	2.40	15.8	6.58	100
3 days and 6 days	2.22	4.1	1.85	97

two-day. There is a slight further increase in all three forms of behavior recorded but, especially in the case of crossings, the differences are not reliable. The chief difference between this and the preceding group is to be

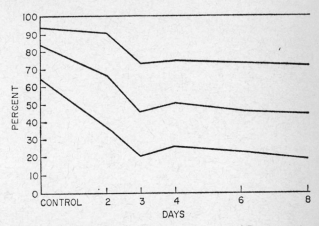

Fig. 3. Showing temporal distribution of crossings, data for the two sexes being combined. The upper line represents the percentage of crossing which occurred during the first five minutes of the test period. The middle line represents the percentage which occurred during the first ten minutes. The lower line represents the percentage which occurred during the first fifteen minutes. ("Control" should read "O," i.e., no starvation period.)

found in the temporal distribution of crossings during the test period. These are now almost uniformly distributed throughout the period.

The four-day group shows a slightly lower average number of approaches and contacts while the crossings remain practically the same. The crossings are still rather uniformly distributed.

The average number of approaches and contacts for the six-day group is almost the same as for the four-day group but there is a definite drop in the number of crossings, the average being 18.1 for the four-day group and 14.1 for the six-day group. This difference being twice the standard deviation of the difference is not entirely reliable, the chances of a true difference being 98 in 100. When it is noted that the succeeding group shows a further drop there seems reason to suppose that this difference is a real one.

The eight-day group shows a further and decided reduction in the number of crossings. Animals of this group were very weak as shown by their gait and general behavior. There is some selection in the composition of this group since three females and two males died in the course of filling out the group which as usual consisted of ten animals of each sex. In spite of their weakness these animals showed a definite orientation toward the incentive compartment. This is indicated by the fact that although they crossed less frequently than did the animals of the six-day group they approached, and made contact without crossing even more frequently. After observing the behavior of these animals one is tempted to say that the hunger drive is as strong as ever and that reduction in crossings is due to decreased capacity to resist the shock. Starvation may possibly effect not only the animals tendency to approach food but its capacity to undergo electric stimulation.

2. Sex differences in the food-seeking drive

Although the behavior of the two sexes was sufficiently similar to justify their combined treatment in the above section there are certain sex differences worth noting. Figure 1 shows diagrammatically the effect of variation in the starvation period upon the approaches, contacts and crossings, the two sexes being considered together. In terms of crossings, the most significant data, the peak of activity extends from two to four days, there being but insignificant differences between the two, three and four-day groups, and all three groups showing decidedly higher values than those preceding or succeeding them. When, however, the two sexes are treated separately it is seen that each presents a rather clear cut peak, that for the female being at two days and that for the male being at four days. This is shown in Fig. 2. Thus the plateau seen in Fig. 1 is merely the result of combining the curves of the two sexes which show peaks at differ-

ent points. It may well be supposed that the drop for
the longer starvation periods is due to the lowering of
vitality through the lack of nourishment. If so, then it
might be said that this weakening influence affects the
female both sooner and more severely than it does the
male. Starvation periods of three and four days lead to
reduction of crossing in the female whereas in the male
the crossings increase up to four days. This does not explain why it is that a two-day starvation results in somewhat greater activity in the female than in the male.

A sex difference is also seen in the data concerning
contacts and approaches.

Approaches. The 0, two and four-day groups show almost no sex difference. From this point on, however, the
female shows decidedly more activity of this sort than
does the male.

Contacts. The trend in the number of contacts with
various degrees of starvation for the male and the female runs almost exactly parallel, with the female at all
times showing considerable more activity of this sort
than the male.

In terms of approaches and contacts it can thus be
seen that the male at no time displays more activity than
the female, and, in fact, that the reverse is usually the
case, especially in the groups of longer starvation periods.
It might then be said that the orientation of the female
was just as surely directed toward the food as in the
case of the male; furthermore, that the more decided
drop in crossings in the case of the female might therefore be due not to less internal stimulation but to a
greater sensitivity to the shock, due to a more rapid
lowering of physical vigor.

Data on the temporal distribution of activity during
the test period show no significant sex differences and
so are not considered here.

3. A comparison of the results here reported with previ-
ously reported data on food-seeking behavior

The present work cannot be compared in any great
detail with any of the work done previously since none
have made use of technique sufficiently like that used
here. Holden's study is the most nearly comparable.

Moss (4) used so few animals that his quantitative data are of little significance. The procedure which he adopted is not well suited to the problem of the rapidity of the increase in the hunger drive and the period of starvation resulting in a maximum. His longer starvation groups were composed merely of those animals which had not crossed the obstruction when tested after shorter periods of starvation. Nevertheless he appears to conclude that the drive constantly increases with an increase in the period of starvation. Presumably we can conclude, on this principle, that it reaches its maximum at the moment the animal dies of starvation. The present study however, clearly indicates an optimum followed by a decline.

Szymanski (8), studying the effect of the length of starvation upon the rate of learning a problem involving a food reward found increased efficiency with increased starvation periods. The longest period he used was, however, twenty-four hours so it seems doubtful whether his studies included the optimal period.

Dodson (1), studying the effect of variation in the length of starvation upon the formation of a visual habit found an optimal point at 41 hours. Animals starved for this period learned more rapidly than those starved for periods of 24, 31 or 48 hours. The differences, however, are not great. Furthermore he made use of animals of but 78 days of age. It might well be expected that such young animals would feel the deleterious effects of starvation sooner than would the 185 day old animals used in the present study.

The effect of starvation periods upon the amount of activity registered by a rat in a freely revolving drum has been noted by Richter (6). Of the eight animals used in the starvation experiment four were deprived of water as well as food and are therefore not comparable to ours. Of the other four animals, two showed a peak of activity after two days of starvation, one after one day while the last animal showed constant decrease in activity after the removal of the food. Unfortunately neither the ages nor the weights of the animals are given.

Nicholls (5) using the same method on the guinea-pig found the peak of activity on the second day followed by a decrease.

The work of Holden (2) is more nearly comparable to the present investigation than any other. Since her results are quite different it seems worth while to enumerate the differences in methodology between her work and this.

The apparatus as used in the present work included the following features not found in Holden's: a tunnel-shaped obstruction compartment provided with manually operated doors at the end, a non-shortcircuiting stimulation grid, a restraining compartment and automatic door built for the purpose of restraining the stimulus animal in the study of the sex drive (but used throughout the present work), an illumination hood providing a constant source of light which threw no shadows.

The animals used in the present work were of the experimental colony strain of the Wistar Institute of Anatomy. They had been raised until the age of 150 days with the sexes unsegregated. They were fed while in this laboratory on a modification of McCollum's standard mixture, which mixture was used as the incentive in the experimentation. They were 185 days of age when tested. Holden's animals were purchased from Douredoure, Philadelphia. They were raised with the sexes segregated. They were fed on bread and milk, which food was used as the incentive in the experimentation. They were 50-60 days of age when tested.

Several differences in procedure should be noted. Holden gave the animals preliminary training on three successive days prior to the test, rather than immediately preceding it, and to groups of ten animals at once rather than to each singly. The test period was ten minutes rather than twenty minutes in length. Holden used three degrees of shock, the lowest of which was much greater than that used in the present study, 1200 volts rather than 475 (the external resistance in the circuit being the same in both cases). Only those results of Holden's concerned with the lowest degree of shock will be considered here since the other degrees of shock did not yield reliable data from the present standpoint.

Using starvation intervals of 0, 12, 24, 36, 48, 60 and 72 hours Holden found a constant increase in the number of crossings up to the 36 hour period which represents the peak of the curve. Further increase in the interval gave constantly decreasing crossing. The absolute values reported are entirely different from those found in the present investigation. For example, the animals of the 36 hour group crossed on the average 40.3 times in the ten-minute test period. Using test periods *twice* this long we found that the most frequently any animal of any group crossed was 36 times and that the highest group average was 19.1. The decided difference in absolute values reported must be due to the radical differences in apparatus and procedure. That Holden found the peak of activity at 36 hours and almost complete reduction of activity for those starvation periods which in the present investigation resulted in the greatest activity is probably accounted for by the fact that the animals she used were immature while those used in our work were full grown.

4. A comparison of the hunger drive (on the basis of the data here reported) and the sex drive (on the basis of data previously reported)

No effort has been spared in these two studies to obtain data which could justly be compared. Animals of the same stock and age were used. The general conditions, feeding, social and so on were the same. The same apparatus was used and no differences in procedure or technique were introduced. All the data for both studies were taken by the same investigator and he made every effort to handle the animals and the apparatus in a uniform way throughout. The method of handling animals in experimental work has been given little consideration in the past. Perhaps in studies of maze learning it matters little whether the rat is lifted by the tail or otherwise. It is the writer's opinion that in the study of animal drives too much care cannot be taken on this point. Slight emotional disturbances may not seriously prolong the rat's learning of a maze but it will serve decidedly to alter the behavior of the animal toward an incentive object. A criticism to be raised against the obstruction method in particular is that results obtained by it are too readily influenced by the technique of the individual investigator in handling the animals. If comparable data are to be obtained by two investigators it seems almost essential that they work together for a time in order that they may adopt the same manner and rhythm of handling the animals. The details of this technique are difficult to transmit exactly in writing. An attempt has been made to enumerate the important points in the report of the study of sex behavior.

The value of the obstruction, i.e., the physical characteristics of the current in the grid, was the same in the study of the two drives. In brief, the only variable consisted in the type of incentive used, food in the one case and sex object in the other.

In the study of the hunger drive the physiological condition most closely related to this phenomenon (the effect of starvation) was varied in order that the optimal condition might be determined. The same holds for the study of the sex drive although the physiological conditions most intimately involved in this case were not the same for the male and the female. With the male it depended upon the length of the sex deprivation interval, with the female it depended upon the oestrus condition.

In the study of the hunger drive the sex factor was kept constant and at the minimum in the two sexes, in the case of the male by using a long deprivation interval and in the case of the female by using only animals in dioestrum. Similarly in the study of the sex drive the food-seeking factor was kept constant and at the minimum by testing the animals immediately after removal from a cage in which there had always been sufficient food.

a. Comparison of the two drives in the male animal. Fairly to compare the two drives in the male we must compare those two groups which represent each drive at the optimum, i.e., those groups which displayed the maximum activity directed toward the incentive in each case. Naturally, it would not do to compare a food-seeking group of a given starvation period with a sex group of a sex deprivation period of the same length, since our results show that the two drives do not recover their strength after a period of satisfaction at the same rate. The sex drive recovers much the more rapidly, reaching its maximum again in about 24 hours, whereas the hunger drive does not reach its peak until about the fourth day. It is the peaks of the two curves which should be compared or at any rate those two groups which, of those tested by us, represent the drives at their maximum. Our interest is in the limits of behavior as influenced by each of these factors and how these limits compare. The four-day starvation group in the case of the hunger drive and the one day sex deprivation group in the case of the sex drive represent these limits in the male. These data are brought together in Tables 7, 8 and 9. It will be seen that the average number of crossings to the sex object was 13.45, to the food, 19.1. This difference is quite a reliable one, being 2.8 times the standard deviation of the difference. We feel justified, then, in saying that, using the obstruction method, the hunger drive is stronger than the sex drive in the male animal.

   b. Comparison of the two drives in the female animal. Here again we must compare those groups representing the two drives at their high points. These are the one-day starvation group in the case of the hunger drive and the cornified group in the case of the sex drive (see Tables 7, 8 and 9). As in the case of the male there is a difference in favor of the hunger drive. This difference is not entirely reliable being 1.7 times the standard deviation of the difference (chances of a true difference: 96 in 100).

   c. Comparison of the two drives, data for the two sexes being combined. As would be expected, when the data for the male and the female groups are combined the difference between the strength of the two drives as here measured is a reliable one. The hunger drive is clearly stronger than the sex drive (Tables 7, 8 and 9).

   This conclusion is in accord with that of Tsai (9) who used the choice method and with that of Simmons (7) who used the learning method. Since all data, in so far as they are interpreted in terms of general tendencies such as drives, are functions of the method used there is good reason for attacking problems by means of any and

TABLE 7

DISTRIBUTION TABLE OF THOSE GROUPS WHICH REPRESENT THE SEX DRIVE AND THE HUNGER DRIVE IN THE MALE AND IN THE FEMALE AT THE OPTIMUM. SEX DRIVE IN THE MALE IS REPRESENTED BY THE ONE-WAY SEX DEPRIVATION GROUP; SEX DRIVE IN THE FEMALE, BY THE GROUP OF ANIMALS TESTED WHEN IN OESTRUM (THE STAGE OF CORNIFIED CELLS); HUNGER DRIVE IN THE MALE, BY THE FOUR-DAY STARVATION GROUP; FOOD-SEEKING DRIVE IN THE FEMALE, BY THE TWO-DAY STARVATION GROUP. DISTRIBUTIONS FOR THE TWO GROUPS REPRESENTING THE SEX DRIVE HAVE BEEN COMBINED AS HAVE ALSO THE DISTRIBUTIONS FOR THE TWO GROUPS REPRESENTING THE HUNGER DRIVE. THESE COMBINED DISTRIBUTIONS HAVE BEEN PLACED SIDE BY SIDE IN THE CENTER FOR READY COMPARISON

INTERVAL	SEX DRIVE IN MALE	SEX DRIVE IN FEMALE	SEX DRIVE, TWO SEXES COMBINED	HUNGER DRIVE, TWO SEXES COMBINED	HUNGER DRIVE IN MALE	HUNGER DRIVE IN FEMALE
0						
1						
2		1	1			
3				1		1
4	1	1	2			
5		1	1	1		1
6	1		1			
7						
8						
9	2	1	3			
10				2	2	
11	2	1	3			
12	1		1			
13	2		2			
14		3	3			
15	4	2	6	2	1	1
16	3	3	6			
17	1	2	3	1		1
18	2	1	3	3	2	1
19		2	2			
20	1		1			
21		2	2	2	1	1
22				1	1	
23				1	1	
24		1	1			
25				2	1	1
26						
27						
28				1		1
29				3	1	2

TABLE 8

SHOWING THE NUMBER OF ANIMALS IN EACH GROUP, THE AVERAGE NUMBER OF CROSSINGS AND THE STANDARD DEVIATIONS FOR THOSE GROUPS TAKEN TO REPRESENT THE SEX AND THE HUNGER DRIVES IN THE TWO SEXES

GROUPS	NUMBER OF ANIMALS IN THE GROUP	AVERAGE NUMBER OF CROSSINGS	STANDARD DEVIATION
Sex drive in male	20	13.45	4.3
Sex drive in female	21	14.14	5.5
Sex drive in two sexes combined	41	13.8	4.9
Hunger drive in male	10	19.1	5.87
Hunger drive in female	10	19.0	8.91
Hunger drive in two sexes combined	20	19.05	7.6

all methods at our disposal. Nevertheless we feel that the results here reported are important not merely because they have been obtained by a different method but also because they have been obtained by a more reliable method than any others which have been employed.

Using the learning method as Simmons did the problem to be solved is a distraction which serves to reduce the prominence of the incentive object in the entire stimulus situation. This reduces the possibility of various incentives producing clear cut differences in the animal's behavior. A minimum amount of learning is involved in the obstruction method as here used. A very simple association is formed in the preliminary trials, that between the incentive object and the incentive compartment. In the course of developing the technique used in these two investigations data were obtained which indicated that the brief preliminary training period used is quite

TABLE 9

SHOWING RELIABILITY OF DIFFERENCES IN THE AVERAGE NUMBER OF CROSSINGS FOR THE SEX AND THE HUNGER DRIVES IN THE TWO SEXES TAKEN SEPARATELY AND COMBINED

GROUPS	STANDARD DEVIATION OF THE DIFFERENCE	THE DIFFERENCE	DIFF./S.D. OF DIFFERENCE	CHANCES IN 100 OF A TRUE DIFFERENCE
Sex drive in male and hunger drive in male	2.0	5.65	2.8	99.74
Sex drive in female and hunger drive in female	2.9	4.91	1.7	96
Sex drive in the two sexes and hunger drive in the two sexes	1.86	5.25	2.8	99.74

as effective as is a much longer one. As tested by the obstruction method the animal is presented with a stimulus situation in which the incentive is dominant. It is not distracted by the complexities of threading a maze or solving other problems, before being stimulated by the object which will call out the drive under investigation.

The choice method does not suffer so much from involving considerable learning. Two simple associations must be formed, however, instead of the one demanded by the obstruction method, and the actual movement of the animal is less simple. Furthermore it seems probable that chance or uncontrolled factors must always play an important part in the choice method. The animal frequently responds simply to whichever incentive happens to stimulate it first in spite of the experimenter's efforts to have the two incentives stimulate it simultaneously and equally. The choice method suffers from a further and more serious difficulty which was apparently not recognized by either Moss or Tsai. To obtain a choice which is to represent a fair comparison between the two drives each acting at its optimum it would be necessary to control, simultaneously, the related physiological conditions. In the case of the female this would involve prediction of oestrous condition, no simple task, and one in which manipulation of the animal prior to testing could scarcely be avoided. In the case of the male it is true that, perhaps on the basis of the results reported herein, one could start the period of starvation at one time and the period of sex deprivation, in the same animal, at another in such a way that theoretically the two drives would reach their optimal points simultaneously. It is improbable, however, that the physiological conditions affecting the two drives are entirely independent of each other. Starvation would affect sex behavior; mating would affect food-seeking behavior. Each drive would be tested under the artificial conditions imposed by the control of the other.

SUMMARY

1. The tendency of the male white rat to approach food as measured in terms of the number of times it will cross an electrical obstruction within a given period of

time is at its low point when the animal is tested immediately after being removed from a cage containing food.
This tendency increases with an increase in the length
of the starvation period, up to a period of four days, and
from this point on, decreases.

2. In the case of the female white rat this tendency
reaches its high point much earlier. The tendency after
one day of starvation is apparently almost as strong as
it is in the male after a four-day period of starvation.
After one day of starvation the tendency in the female
declines gradually and then more rapidly, never after the
second day being as strong as in the male.

3. Comparison of the groups which, of those tested,
represent the hunger and the sex drives at their maximum, indicates that the tendency for a white rat to approach a food object is stronger than its tendency to approach a sex object. This is true of rats of both sexes although the difference is not so great in the case of the
female.

REFERENCES

1. Dodson, J. D. 1917. Relative values of reward and punishment in habit formation. Psychobiology, i, 231-276.
2. Holden, F. 1926. A study of the effect of starvation upon
   behavior by means of the obstruction method. Comp.
   Psych. Monog., iii, no. 17, pp. 45.
3. Jenkins, T. N., Warner, L. H., and Warden, C. J. 1926.
   Standard apparatus for the study of animal motivation.
   Jour. Comp. Psych., vi, 361-382.
4. Moss, F. A. 1924. A study of animal drives. Jour. Exp.
   Psych., vii, 165-185.
5. Nicholls, E. E. 1922. A study of the spontaneous activity in the guinea-pig. Jour. Comp. Psych., ii, 303-330.
6. Richter, C. P. 1922. A behavioristic study of the rat.
   Comp. Psych. Monog., i, no. 2, pp. 55.
7. Simmons, R. 1924. The relative effectiveness of certain
   incentives on animal learning. Comp. Psych. Monog., ii,
   no. 7, pp. 79.
8. Szymanski, J. S. 1919. Die Abhangigheit des Lerngesch-
   windigkeit von der Antriebsstärke. Pflüg. Arch. f. d. gesamte
   Physiol., clxxiii, 141-148.

9. TSAI, C. 1925. The relation of the sex and hunger motives in the albino rat. Jour. Comp. Psych., v, 407-415.

10. WARNER, L. H. 1927. A study of sex behavior in the white rat by means of the obstruction method. Comp. Psych. Monog., iv, no. 22. 68 pp.

11. WARNER, L. H. 1928. A study of thirst behavior in the white rat by means of the obstruction method. Jour. Genetic Psych., xxxv, forthcoming number.

9

Changes in Hunger During Starvation

W. T. HERON AND B. F. SKINNER*
University of Minnesota

The view that drive could be specified in terms of hours of deprivation was further reinforced by the work of Heron and Skinner. Their study shows that deprivation intervals up to three or four days are linearly related to bar pressing for a food reinforcement.

The following selection is reprinted from The Psychological Record, 1937, 1, 51-60, *with the permission of the authors and the journal.*

An important problem in the study of behavior is the relation of the degree of hunger to the period of deprivation of food. What is the maximal degree to be obtained during starvation, and how is it related to the degrees prevailing under current experimental procedures of controlling the drive? If the maximal degree can be ascertained, it is possible to express any degree as a percentage of the maximum and hence on an absolute scale. It is then also possible to compare drives associated with different kinds of reinforcement (e.g., sex or thirst).

A convenient measure of hunger in the white rat may be derived from the fact that when a conditioned response is reinforced periodically, the rate at which it is elicited without reinforcement varies with the state of the drive.[1] For example, where the drive is hunger, the rate is modified in a definite way by the ingestion of given amounts of food. The greatest degree of hunger ex-

* Manuscript recommended for publication by Dr. J. R. Kantor, April 10, 1937.
[1] Skinner, B. F., Conditioning and Extinction and their Relation to Drive, Jour. Gen. Psychol., 1936, 14, 296-317.

amined in the paper cited was that which prevails just before feeding when a rat is allowed to eat freely for a limited time once a day. The degrees which proved to be dependent upon the ingestion of different amounts of food were below this value, but the rate should also reflect changes in hunger above it.

The procedure of investigating hunger during deprivation is simple. Food is withheld from the organism and the state of the drive measured frequently enough to follow the course of the change with accuracy. The use of a conditional reflex is complicated by the necessity of reinforcing the response to avoid extinction. The reinforcement must involve a consummatory response, and this modifies the drive to some extent. The periodic reinforcement in the present case requires that the organism receive a small amount of food whenever the strength of the drive is measured. The alternative would be to take only one measurement per rat and to obtain the course of the change in terms of the averages for groups deprived of food for different periods. But it will be shown that the rates at which hunger increases during starvation vary quite widely among rats and that an average curve does not reflect the course of the change in the individual case. The first alternative is, therefore, to be preferred even though it does not represent the case for complete deprivation. The amount of food actually ingested in the present experiment was less than one gram per day and probably had but little effect upon the result.

SUBJECTS AND TECHNIQUE

Sixteen animals, all males, were started in the experiment. One animal was eliminated very soon because it was found to have defective teeth. The results for two other animals are not included because they were accidentally given access to food. The data which will follow are based upon the remaining thirteen rats.

They were about 150 days of age, with the exception of four which were about 100 days old at the start of the experiment. The subjects were originally grouped in sets of four each. This grouping was maintained throughout the experiment although some of the groups were not full owing to the eliminations mentioned above.

The apparatus and method were essentially as described in the paper cited. The response to be made by the rat was the pressing downward of a light horizontal bar or lever. A clock connected the lever and a food magazine in such a way that a response was reinforced with a small pellet of food every four minutes. All responses were recorded in summation curves. The experimental periods were one hour long and occurred at the same time each day. The first group was started at 8:15 A.M. and the successive groups were run as rapidly as possible, finishing at about 12:30 P.M. The rats were kept in a constant temperature cabinet set at 25° C. Water was available at all times.

On the day previous to the initiation of the starvation period, the rats were allowed continuous access to food for 24 hours. From that time on they were allowed no food save that which was necessary to recondition them. Since the interval of reconditioning was four minutes and the daily test period one hour, each animal received a daily ration of about 15 pellets or a total mass of approximately 0.7 grams.

Under these conditions the animals were tested daily until death by starvation. It was not originally intended to carry the experiment so far as this, but by the time the course of the change had been clearly worked out in each case the animal could not be salvaged.

RESULTS

In general terms, the results may be stated as follows: As measured by the number of responses to the lever per hour, hunger increases with the period of starvation until a maximal degree is reached. After this point there is a relatively rapid decline in the rate of responding until death ensues from inanition.

Figure 1 is a graph showing the daily mean number of responses. Since there are individual differences in regard to the day on which the maximal rate is reached, the interpretation is somewhat difficult. The rat which reached its maximal rate first did so on the fourth day while at the other extreme one rat prolonged its rise to the thirteenth day after the beginning of the starvation period (see Fig. 4). If this difficulty is disregarded and

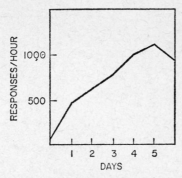

Fig. 1. The change in the mean rate of responding during starvation. The point at zero is for the rate after twenty-four hours of continuous access to food. The rate rises rapidly during the first twenty-four hours and continues more slowly but in a roughly linear fashion until a peak is reached on the fifth day. The curve represents thirteen rats. It is not continued after the sixth day because the group was no longer intact.

if we assume that there is a direct relationship between the rate of responding and the strength of drive, the mean maximal drive for the group occurred on the fifth day after the beginning of the starvation period.

Figure 1 also indicates that the relationship between the increase in mean drive and the progress of inanition is approximately linear until the peak is reached. The greatest deviation from linearity is the relatively abrupt rise between the first and second points on the curve, but this is an artifact due to the fact that the first period was preceded by a 24-hour period of continuous access to the food.

The curve in Fig. 1 has been plotted only to the sixth day after the beginning of starvation. A number of animals continued in the experiment after this point but several also died before the seventh day's record was taken. It would be misleading to continue this curve since it would no longer be representative of the group as a whole.

Because of the individual differences with respect to the time at which the peak is reached, it was thought desirable to superimpose the individual records at their maximal rates. This was done in the following way. The point of the beginning of the experiment and the point of reaching a peak were indicated on a sheet of graph paper. The distance between them was then divided into a number of equal parts corresponding to the number of days taken to reach the peak by one rat. The data for this rat were then plotted and the points connected by straight lines. The data for each rat were treated in the same way. Ordinates were then erected to divide each of the individual curves into eight equal parts. The intersections of the ordinates with the individual curves were read off on each vertical and averaged. The curves in Fig. 2 (solid lines) are for the averages thus obtained.

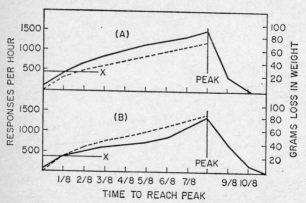

Fig. 2. The change in mean rate and in body-weight when the individual series are superimposed to bring their peaks together. Solid lines: rate; dashed lines: loss in weight. The increase in rate follows the loss in weight fairly closely. Group A (eight rats) shows a more rapid decline after the peak than Group B (five rats). The mean peak is higher and is reached somewhat sooner by Group A. The horizontal lines marked X indicate the rate prevailing at "normal" hunger (see text).

The parts of the curves beyond the peaks were also spaced out on the coordinates assigned to each rat and the averages obtained in the same way. Because of the fact that there was some individual variation in the amount of time elapsing between the attainment of the peak and death, the portions of the curves to the right of the peaks are not representative of the whole group throughout their entire length.

Before the group curves were made by the method described immediately above, the daily records were plotted for each rat. An inspection of the individual curves indicated that it would be convenient to deal with the records in two groups. The first group (A in Fig. 2) is composed of the eight animals which rose to their maximal rate and then dropped precipitously back towards zero.

The second group is composed of the remaining five animals, the curve for which is shown as B in Fig. 2. They maintained a lower mean rate for the first six-eighths of the time. Their rate from that time on increased more rapidly until they reached a peak, which was not as high as that reached by the first group. Their rate after the peak does not decline so rapidly and their mean survival time is longer.

The differences in these two curves may or may not indicate a fundamental difference in the animals involved. In any case it should be pointed out that the difference after the peak may be an artifact caused by the fact that a continuous process was sampled at the relatively gross intervals of 24 hours. For example, in the rats which are represented in curve B, the drive may have reached its maximal rate in the 24-hour interval elapsing between the test period showing the highest rate and the next test period. In other words, the peak shown on the curve is possibly misplaced to the left of its true position. This difficulty is inherent in the present technique, but it could be minimized by using shorter test periods spaced at closer intervals. After each animal had passed its peak, it was obvious that it was in an extremely impoverished condition. It was cold to the touch (bodily temperatures were not taken), its hair was erect and shaggy, and in many cases a normal posture could not be maintained. From these observations and from the early death of the animal after its peak was reached, it may be possible that the decline in rate of responding was due to physical weakness, rather than to any independent decrease in the state of the drive. The experiments do not confirm the human report of an early decrease in hunger during prolonged fasting.

The two lines drawn parallel with the base line marked X in Fig. 2 indicate the rate of response under the usual feeding method [2] as determined for the respective groups before the beginning of the starvation period. It is obvious that the level of drive maintained by the usual feeding method is far below the maximal strength.

The dashed curves in Fig. 2 represent the absolute loss in weight for the two groups. Each rat was weighed daily after each test period and the loss of weight calculated. The data thus secured were plotted in the same way as the rates of responding, letting the end point for each rat's weight curve be determined by the day on which he reached his maximal rate of responding. An inspection of Fig. 2 shows that the correspondence between the mean loss of weight and the mean rate of responding is very close.

Figure 3 is reproduced to give the reader a photostatic copy of the type of record which is obtained on successive days. The curve at A is the record made by the animal after the 24 hours of continuous access to food. Since the animal was almost satiated, its rate was very low. The record at B is that which the animal made after one day of starvation and is approximately the rate maintained under the usual feeding method. The remaining records are for the successive days of starvation until the animal reached its peak on the fifth day (curve F). This animal belongs to the first group spoken of above and did not survive to give a record on the day following his peak.

Figure 4 gives some of the significant measurements on

[2] With the 'usual feeding method' each rat is allowed access to the food for 1½ hours each day after the experimental period. The food used is Purina Dog Chow in large checkers. The small pellets used for re-inforcement were manufactured from this commercial food.

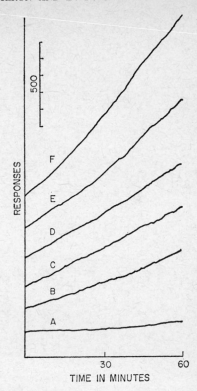

Fig. 3. A representative series of records for one of the rats in Group A. The record at A was taken after twenty-four hours of continuous access to food. Records B, C, D, . . . follow at twenty-four hour intervals during starvation. The slight acceleration in Curves E and F is not typical.

individual rats. The maximal rates are presented in terms of responses per hour on the day at which a peak was reached. The time to death is given as the number of days of starvation after which records were obtained. "Six days before death" means that the rat was dead on the seventh experimental day after food was withdrawn.

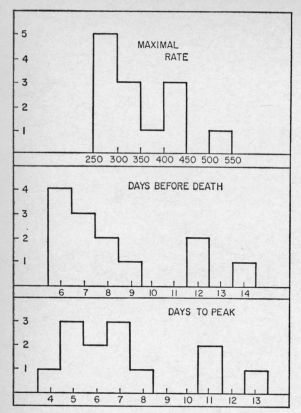

Fig. 4. Distributions of maximal rates, times to death, and times to peak.

DISCUSSION

A comprehensive investigation has been conducted in the Columbia University laboratory with the aim of ranking various drives in order of strength.[3] Since it is necessary that all drives be measured in comparable units, the maximal strength of each drive was ascertained by com-

[3] See Warden, C. J., Animal motivation: experimental studies on the albino rat. New York: Columbia University Press. 1931.

paring the strength of a conditioned response based upon the drive with an opposed response of supposedly constant strength. The drives were ranked on the basis of the maximal strengths so obtained. The course of the change in strength of each drive was followed by using separate groups of animals with varying degrees of deprivation. For example, in the investigation of hunger (experiments by Warner) six groups of twenty rats each were used. One group was measured after no days of starvation, another after two days, and so on for three, four, six, and eight days of deprivation. For male rats the group which had had four days of deprivation exhibited the largest number of responses prepotent over the opposed response. Measured with the present method the hunger drive reaches its maximum on the fifth day of deprivation (see Fig. 1). The difference of one day may be caused by the fact that it was necessary in the present experiment to give a small amount of food for reinforcement. In general, the results check rather closely.

It is significant, however, that in the present experiment the measure obtained from averaging the group to represent the maximal drive is depressed. This is presumably also true of the Columbia experiments. There are individual differences with reference to the point at which the rats reach their maximal drive during the period of deprivation. For example, in the experiment cited, some of the rats which were starved for four days had probably reached their maximal drive before the test period and some certainly reached it afterwards. The fourth day happens to catch more of the animals at or near their maximal drive than any other period used. An inspection of the data from the present experiment shows that the animals ranged from the fourth to the thirteenth day of starvation in reaching their peak. The mean is at 7.3 days and the median is 7. A comparison of the height of the peak in Fig. 1 with the height of the peaks in Fig. 2 will illustrate the depressing effect which the averaging of the group without respect to individual maxima has upon that peak.

This difficulty would not be serious if the measurements of all drives were affected in the same way, but unfortunately this is not the case. There are certain conditions under which the depressing effect will be mini-mized. (1) If the drive rises very rapidly to a peak (cf. thirst) the method of averaging groups will catch a great many more animals at or near their peak than would be the case if the drive rose slowly to a climax as in the case of hunger. (2) if the drive is maintained at the peak for a relatively long time, the chances of catching all animals at or near a peak value are very good. An ex-ample is the maternal drive which is probably maintained at its maximal level for a number of days while a litter is young.

This criticism of the use of one measurement per rat, and of the necessary averaging of group values in deter-mining the course of a change in drive would, if true, in-validate a ranking of drives in the order of strength. Sup-pose that one is comparing hunger and thirst. The meas-ure of thirst closely approximates the true maximal strength of that drive but the measure of hunger is con-siderably below the value actually obtaining in individual cases. It may be that the hunger drive is actually weaker than the thirst drive; if so the method has exaggerated the difference. Or it may be that the hunger drive is actually stronger than the thirst drive, but because the mean for the hunger drive has been depressed, it ap-pears to be weaker. If maximal drives are to be com-pared in strength, the comparison should be based upon the mean individual peak.

SUMMARY

The course of the change in hunger during starvation was followed by examining the rate at which a rat re-sponded to a lever when a response was reinforced with a small pellet of food every four minutes. Measurements were made for one hour at twenty-four hour intervals. The mean rate for a group of thirteen rats reached a peak at five days of starvation. The individual records showed greater peak rates reached at from four to fourteen days. The mean rate was found not to be a reliable indication of the extent or the course of hunger in the individual. The typical curve for a single rat shows a steady rise throughout the greater part of the period before death. The ultimate drop is precipitous and coincides with a drop in bodily temperature and the general debilitation of the rat.

10

Deprivation and Time of Testing as Determinants of Food Intake[1]

JOHN K. BARE
Carleton College

and GEORGE CICALA
Princeton University

The following selection points to one difficulty frequently encountered when one varies drive in terms of hours of deprivation. The normal day-night behavior cycle persists even following prolonged deprivation. ✓

The following selection is reprinted from The Journal of Comparative and Physiological Psychology, 1960, 53, 151-154, *with the permission of the authors and the American Psychological Association.*

An analysis of the operation of food deprivation reveals that there are three variables involved: (*a*) the duration of the deprivation, (*b*) the time of day at which food is removed, and (*c*) the time of day at which food is restored (for convenience of expression, time of testing). It is further evident that for values other than multiples of 24 hr., the duration of the deprivation, probably the most important variable, will inevitably be confounded with one of the other two.

In a previous study, the time of day at which food was removed was held constant, a single deprivation was employed for purposes of simplification, and the subsequent

[1] Based in part upon a thesis submitted by the junior author to the College of William and Mary in partial fulfillment of the requirement for the degree of Master of Arts. This research was supported by Grant G-4460, National Science Foundation, and by Grant M-2959, National Institute of Mental Health, Public Health Service.

food intake was measured for 24 hr. to provide a complete description of the behavior (Bare, 1959). The findings were most unusual. During the first hour of eating, time of testing interacted with length of deprivation in such a way that the function relating intake to deprivation was *not* monotonic, and further analysis suggested that the time of testing reflected the well-established, cyclic, day-night pattern (e.g., Siegel & Stuckey, 1947); during the subsequent 23 hr. of measurement, intake was identical with that of undeprived animals, in terms of both the amount and the pattern. Thus animals deprived for 18 hr. ate less than those deprived for 2 hr.; animals deprived for 24 hr. failed to replace their food deficit.

But the data did not permit a precise statement of the way in which time of testing modifies the function relating intake to deprivation. In the present study, length of deprivation is permitted to be confounded with the time of day at which food is removed, for such conditions probably approximate those normally employed by investigators manipulating the hunger drive. Then for each of several values of length of deprivation, ranging from 0 to 24 hr., intake could be measured at two different times of testing, 7 P.M. and 1 P.M., representing times of high and low intake in normal animals. Such a design permits the uncontaminated assessment of the contribution of the time-of-testing variable.

METHOD

Fifty-six male white rats, averaging three and one-half months of age and 333 gm., served as Ss. The apparatus and procedure have been previously described in detail (Bare, 1959), but in brief, a Skinner-type apparatus was enclosed in a sound-dampening box, and cumulative recorders were employed. The animal obtained its food by performing a continuously reinforced bar-pressing response, and water was available at all times.

Following a single deprivation of 24 hr., the animals were trained and then permitted to become accustomed to this method of feeding for 72 hr. prior to the introduction of the experimental variables. Seven values of deprivation were used, 0, 2, 4, 8, 12, 18, or 24 hr., and for each there were two times of testing, 1 P.M. or 7 P.M. Thus, there were 14 groups of animals, four in each group. Four identical boxes were available, and each box was employed once for each group. Following deprivation, food intake was measured continuously for 24 hr.

In order to make the findings applicable to the usual laboratory conditions of deprivation, the temperature was permitted to decrease during the dark hours and to rise during the daylight. Temperatures ranged 66° to 79°F., with a few unavoidable exceptions. It was also desired that the animal experience the normal changes in daylight and darkness. Inasmuch as the experiment continued over a period of five months, some control over seasonal changes in daylight was obtained by securing data for all values of deprivation and time of testing, and then replicating. The replications also provided some control for day-to-day temperature fluctuations.

RESULTS

Figure 1 presents the cumulative intake in pellets during the 24 hr. following deprivation for those animals

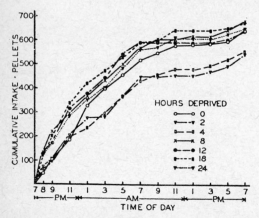

Fig. 1. Twenty-four-hour intake following deprivation. (Time of testing [food restored]: 7 P.M.)

tested at 7 P.M. Amount of deprivation is the parameter. Figure 2 presents similar data for those animals tested at 1 P.M. It appears from both figures, but particularly from Fig. 2, that the major response to the deprivation occurred during the first hour of measurement. Thereafter, intake for all groups was comparable, and all groups displayed the day-night cycle differences in food intake. It should perhaps be noted, in addition, that during the 24-hr. measurement period, the 24-hr.-deprived groups did not double their food intake, thus failing to repair the food deficit.

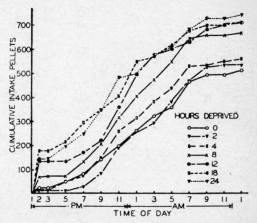

Fig. 2. Twenty-four-hour intake following deprivation. (Time of testing [food restored]: 1 P.M.)

If one examines in greater detail the intake during the first hour, a problem is immediately apparent. Of the animals whose food is restored at 1 P.M., 9 of the 16 animals in the 0-, 2-, 4-, and 8-hr. groups failed to eat during the first hour of measurement, and 1 animal in the 0-hr., 7 P.M. group also failed to eat. As a consequence, intake during the first hour of eating, whenever that occurred, was used as the datum. Analysis of these data indicated that it was the first meal which the animal eats that comprised the response to the deprivation. (A meal was defined in this case as the ingestion of at least four pellets, followed by a rest pause of at least 10 min.) Indeed, if the intake during this first meal is subtracted from the intake during the 24-hr. measurement period, there are no differences among the various groups.

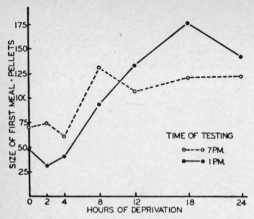

Fig. 3. *The effect of deprivation on the size of the first meal, with time of testing as the parameter.*

Figure 3 displays the size of the first meal as a function of length of deprivation, with time of testing as the parameter. A complex analysis of variance reveals that deprivation was the only significant variable, as indicated in Table 1.

But the shape of the curves in Fig. 3 suggests that some interaction is present. For each time of testing, the data for the first meal for the 0-, 2-, and 4-hr. deprivation groups were combined into a "Low" deprivation group, and the data for the 12-, 18-, and 24-hr. groups were

TABLE 1

SUMMARY OF ANALYSIS OF VARIANCE OF THE
MEAN NUMBER OF PELLETS, FIRST MEAL,
ALL DEPRIVATION GROUPS

Source	df	MS	F
Time of Testing	1	111	.05
Deprivation	6	13,615	6.15*
TT × D	6	2,805	1.27
Within Groups	42	2,214	—

* $p < .005$.

combined to form a "High" deprivation group, with the median value of 8 hr. of deprivation omitted. The mean values for these groups in pellets were: Low—1 P.M., 40.1; Low—7 P.M., 68.7; High—1 P.M., 151.2; and High —7 P.M., 116.7. A complex analysis of variance then indicated that both deprivation and the interaction between deprivation and time of testing were significant. Table 2 presents the results of this second analysis. Sub-

TABLE 2

SUMMARY OF ANALYSIS OF VARIANCE OF THE
MEAN NUMBER OF PELLETS, FIRST MEAL,
LOW AND HIGH DEPRIVATION GROUPS

Source	df	MS	F
Time of Testing	1	105	.08
Deprivation	1	75,923	60.55*
TT × D	1	11,913	9.50*
Within Groups	44	1,254	—

* $p < .005$.

sequent t's between group means, using the within-groups mean square for the computation of the standard error of the difference indicated that the p's associated with the differences between all means is less than .05, except for the difference between the Low—7 P.M. and the Low—1 P.M., in which case $p < .10 > .05$.

No other feature of the eating behavior was altered significantly by variables under consideration, i.e., neither rate of eating nor the duration of the meal was changed. The apparent paradoxical nature of these statements is resolved when it is added that the duration of the meal did increase, but not significantly so, and the rate of eating remained virtually constant.

DISCUSSION

It is reassuring to find an approximation of the usual monotonic function relating food intake to length of deprivation, but it must again be concluded that the normal day-night cycle of intake influences ingestion *after* depri-

vation, at least after a single deprivation. The effects of
the cycle are two: (a) during the first meal after deprivation, time of testing alters the slope of the intake-depri-
vation function, and (b) after the first meal, the cycle
dictates what the intake shall be.

A question which naturally arises is whether similar
results would be obtained with longer single deprivations.
In a brief study, the senior author used deprivations of
0, 24, 48, and 72 hr., and the subsequent intake was
measured for 48 hr. There were four animals in each
group. In this case, both the time at which food was
removed and the time of day at which food was restored
could be held constant at 7 P.M. Deprivation increased
intake four- to fivefold during the first hour of eating,
with an apparent asymptote at 24 hr. of deprivation.
Thereafter the cyclic pattern appeared, and during the
remaining 23 hr. of the first day of measurement, deprived animals ate somewhat less than the nondeprived,
so that the total intake for all groups was approximately
the same during the first 24 hr. following deprivation.
On the second day of measurement, the pattern was
again present and the intake for all groups was again approximately equal.

The cycle is persistent and is reflected in the time-of-
testing variable. How shall these findings be understood?
To account for the interaction between length of deprivation and time of testing, one might simply postulate
that because of the differential rate of intake during a 24-
hr. period, different times of testing for a fixed duration
of deprivation actually represent differing amounts of
food loss to the animal. For example, an animal deprived
of food from 7 P.M. to 1 P.M. (18 hr.) has a greater food
loss by weight than an animal deprived from 1 A.M. to
7 P.M. (18 hr.). But such a position fails to encompass
the differences in food intake produced by different times
of testing for 0 and 24 hr. of deprivation, where food loss
by weight is constant. Furthermore, a tendency for the
animal to be active and to rest in cycles must underlie
all other behaviors, including drinking, exploration, and
sexual responses, as well as eating. Perhaps it will be necessary to think in terms of several drives, simultaneously
present but varying in momentary strength as a conse-

quence of all the behaviors of the animal (cf. Maslow, 1954). At 1 P.M., larger amounts of deprivation may produce greater intake than at 7 P.M. because the drive to explore does not compete with the drive to eat; and at 1 P.M., smaller amounts of deprivation may produce a smaller intake than at 7 P.M. because the drive to rest competes with the drive to eat. In short, the amount eaten during the first meal is dependent, at least in part, by the momentary strength of all drives.

SUMMARY

The effects of length of deprivation and the time of testing (i.e., the time of day at which food is restored) on food intake were studied in a factorial design. The major response of the animal to deprivation was an increase in the size of the first meal, and the slope of the function relating first-meal size to deprivation was altered by the time-of-testing variable.

REFERENCES

BARE, J. K. Hunger, deprivation, and the day-night cycle. *J. comp. physiol. Psychol.*, 1959, 52, 129-131.

MASLOW, A. H. *Motivation and personality.* New York: Harper, 1954.

SIEGEL, P. S., & STUCKEY, H. L. The diurnal course of water and food intake in the normal mature rat. *J. comp. physiol. Psychol.*, 1947, 40, 365-370.

11

Relation of Random Activity to Food Deprivation

BYRON A. CAMPBELL AND FRED D. SHEFFIELD
Institute of Human Relations, Yale University

Studies have frequently shown that deprived animals are more active than those that are satiated. This fact has led to the general view that behavior is energized or invigorated by drive states. In this selection the authors show that drive does not directly lead to activity, but rather that drive states serve to increase the animal's sensitivity to external stimuli which in turn increases activity.

The selection is reprinted from The Journal of Comparative and Physiological Psychology, *1953, 46, 320-322, with the permission of the authors and the American Psychological Association.*

It is usually taken for granted in textbooks of general psychology that increased "drive" produces increased random activity. For example, Dashiell says in his latest revision of his general text: "The unbalanced state [hunger] drives the organism into activity, and the activity continues until a steady state is restored" (2, p. 141).

It is also commonly assumed that the mechanism by which a drive state increases activity is a strong external or internal stimulus. Thus, pain from external shock has been treated as a typical drive state (3, 4), and activity produced by hunger has been treated as a response to a strong internal stimulus (6).

An alternative mechanism is that drives involve lowered thresholds to external stimulation. This hypothesis would predict little change in activity in an animal in a drive state unless there were some external stimulation. According to this hypothesis the drive state does not force activity; it merely makes the animal more responsive to environmental changes. Previous studies relating hunger drive to activity (e.g., 5, 7) have not made a specific attempt to maintain a constant environment. The main purpose of the present experiment was to compare the random activity of hungry animals before and after a marked environmental change. A second purpose was to relate this comparison to degree of deprivation. A third purpose was to check the hypothesis that drive activity is mediated by an increase in stimulation.

METHOD

The Ss were 12 mature Wistar rats with a weight range from 310 to 410 gm. at the outset of the experiment. The activity measure used was worked out after a good deal of trial and error on a variety of devices for recording activity. The unit finally used has been described elsewhere (1). It consists of a round cage with four sensitive microswitches placed at each of the four quadrants. It is pivoted at the center and has about ⅛-in. clearance in tipping in any direction. It is wired so that any shift in the location of the "tilt" among the four quadrants will advance an electromagnetic counter. The apparatus usually fails to record certain small movements like scratching, but it records larger movements such as moving from one quadrant to another or shaking the cage.

Six of these units were installed in a cabinet soundproofed with Celutex. The cabinet was well ventilated by an exhaust fan, which also dominated the auditory field of the rat. To make doubly sure that auditory stimuli outside the cabinet would not affect Ss, the cabinet was placed in a soundproofed room for the duration of the experiment. The auditory field could be varied by turning off the exhaust fan; the visual field could be controlled by turning on lights inside the two chambers of the cabinet, which were otherwise unlighted.

The animals were put into the cabinet and fed dry Purina pellets ad libitum for four days. They were then starved for three days. At a fixed time (noon) on each of the seven days their activity as recorded by the counters was measured for 10 min., after which an environmental change was introduced and their activity was recorded for another 10 min. The environmental change was both auditory and visual. The continual hum of the exhaust fan in the cabinet was turned off, and the lights in the cabinet were turned on. It should be further noted that the counters recorded—as a base line—the activity of the animals over every 24 hr., exclusive of the two 10-min. tests each day.

RESULTS AND DISCUSSION

The main results are shown in Fig. 1. It can be seen that environmental change has a large effect on the ran-

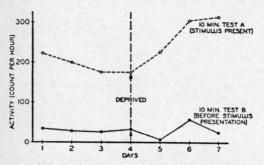

Fig. 1. *The effect of deprivation on the activity response to an environmental change. To facilitate comparison of 10-min. test period activity and total daily activity, the data in Figs. 1 and 2 are plotted in terms of counts per hour. To obtain this measure the activity scores for the 10-min. test periods were multiplied by six and the 24-hr. scores were divided by 24.*

dom activity of Ss. When the fan went off and the lights came on, Ss became more active. This was true whether Ss were satiated as in the first four days or whether they were hungry as in the second three days. This general difference is shown by the high level of the dotted line as contrasted with the solid line. The latter curve shows the mean number of counts per hour in the 10-min. tests before the environmental change. The solid line varies somewhat but seems to hold to a fixed level. The difference is well beyond the .01 level.

It can also be noted in Fig. 1 that Ss show a tendency toward adaptation to the environmental change during the satiation period. They reduced their activity somewhat by the end of four days of adaptation to the cages and the environmental change. But when they are deprived of food, they reverse the adaptation process and show a significant rise in activity in response to an external change as hours of deprivation are increased. The figure shows no noticeable trend toward an increase during the tests given just before the environmental change, even though the animals were starved over three successive days. These results support the idea that hunger drive involves a lowering of thresholds rather than an internal drive stimulus.

A logical implication of this interpretation is that animals should show increased activity with deprivation simply because they are always getting at least some external stimulation. They can feel their own responses, hear their own microswitches whenever they click, and hear the clicking of microswitches of the other two animals in their section of the apparatus. These stimuli should combine to produce an effect similar to the controlled environmental change of fan off and lights on as sources of stimulation producing an increase in activity due to lowered thresholds.

No significant rise was found in the 10-min. "before" tests, but they are not as reliable as the total activity through the 24 hr. of the three-day starvation period. If total activity over successive 24-hr. periods is plotted, a slight but statistically significant rise is found. This is shown by the solid line in Fig. 2, and is compared with

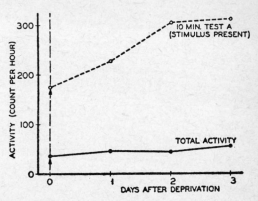

Fig. 2. A comparison of the effects of deprivation on "spontaneous" activity and the activity response to an environmental change.

the effects of the controlled environmental change. The figure shows some increase in activity without any controlled change. The level of activity is much higher with the environmental change, however, and while both go up with deprivation, the increase is much more prominent in the case of a controlled environmental change.

SUMMARY

Random activity of 12 rats was measured for a period of seven days in a constant environment. During the first four days the animals were on an ad libitum diet; during the last three days they were deprived of all food. Activity was automatically recorded over each 24-hr. period. It was also recorded for 10-min. periods before and during a gross change in the auditory and visual environment.

It was found that: (a) an environmental change consistently produced an increase in activity; (b) without the environmental change there was a relatively small increase in activity with deprivation whereas there was a relatively large increase with deprivation during the environmental change.

The main conclusion is that hunger drive seems to involve lowered thresholds of response rather than internal stimulation to activity. The slight rise in general activity as the animals are starved over a three-day period is interpreted as due to their greater sensitivity to minimal stimulus changes in the environment provided. This rise was small relative to the rise in the effects of a large environmental change during the same starvation period. Starvation does not instigate activity; it only lowers the threshold for normal stimuli to activity.

REFERENCES

1. CAMPBELL, B. A. Design and reliability of a new activity recording device. *J. comp. physiol. Psychol.* in press.
2. DASHIELL, J. F. *Fundamentals of general psychology.* Boston: Houghton Mifflin, 1949.

3. Hull, C. L. *Principles of behavior.* New York: Appleton-Century, 1943.
4. Miller, N. E., & Dollard, J. *Social learning and imitation.* New Haven: Yale Univer. Press, 1941.
5. Richter, C. P. Animal behavior and internal drives. *Quart. Rev. Biol.,* 1927, 2, 307-343.
6. Wada, Tomi. An experimental study of hunger in its relation to activity. *Arch. Psychol.,* 1922, No. 57.
7. Wald, G., & Jackson, B. Activity and nutritional deprivation. *Proc. nat. Acad. Sci.,* 1944, 30, 255-263.

12

Eating and Drinking as a Function of Maintenance Schedule

WILLIAM S. VERPLANCK AND JOHN R. HAYES[1]
Harvard University

The following selection illustrates the interrelated nature of drives and shows that food deprivation not only serves to produce a hunger drive, but affects other drive systems as well. In spite of the fact that the psychologist may induce hunger and use food as a reinforcement for the acquisition of new responses, he must recognize that a hungry animal is also a thirsty one. When food deprivation is employed, the organism reduces his water intake, thus creating a thirst drive.

This article is reprinted from The Journal of Comparative and Physiological Psychology, 1953, 46, 327-333, with the permission of the authors and the American Psychological Association.

Animals without water do not eat as much food as usual, and hungry animals do not drink much water (4, 8, 13, 16, 17, 20). Animals drink more after meals than at other times. The dog and hen (13) and the rat (20) show a drop in food intake during water deprivation. Dogs (5, 11) and rats (20) similarly drop in water intake during food deprivation. Rats drink more after a period of water deprivation during which food is available than after a similar period with no food available (17). The corresponding case for food intake apparently has not been investigated. After protracted periods of food or water deprivation, rats exceed in both drinking and eating their average value before deprivation (4).

---

[1] Now at the Massachusetts Institute of Technology.

No systematic sets of data are available in these phenomena as they are encountered in studies of learning, although their significance for theoretical formulations of "motivation" and learning has not escaped some investigators (9, p. 234; 22). Recent studies on "drive interaction," "drive discrimination," and on "cognitions" have involved the control of the behavior of food-deprived and of water-deprived rats by food and water placed in goal boxes and alleys (21). These have not had uniform results, so that it is pertinent to examine the matter more closely.

Today's learning theorists are in fair agreement on a definition of "drive." This concept is an intervening variable, explicitly involving two sets of operations and implicitly a third.[2] The first operations establish drives; e.g., for hunger and thirst, the animal is deprived of food and water, respectively, for a stated number of hours. The second class of operations is the measurement of classes of behavior (running, bar pressing, eating) that vary with the duration of the preceding deprivation. The third, implicit, operation is that of satiation, usually giving the animal access to food and water long enough so that it neither eats nor drinks for a specified period. "Satiation" operations vary considerably.

In this experiment, the operations are depriving the animal of food or water, or both, through stated intervals of time following free feeding and free drinking. The measure of behavior chosen is the total weight, in grams, of food and water ingested by the animal in the first hour following the period of deprivation. The adequacy of these measures has been established by others (1, p. 128; 2, 7, 15, 18, 19).

The general plan of the experiment and the values of the variables investigated have been chosen to provide data useful for the interpretation of experimental data in the field of learning.

---

[2] Hull's 1943 theory of drive (9) is in somewhat different status. Laws relating D to privation and other experimental variables are not incorporated in the theory, but are left stated somewhat casually (e.g., $D = f(h)$ in the supporting text. The details of these relationships were left open, presumably to be filled in empirically.

METHOD

Subjects. Twelve male albino rats (Hisaw strain) ranging in age from 97 to 100 days at the beginning of the first experiment were the Ss. Before the experiment, they were caged in groups of six, with continuous access to food and water.

Experimental room and apparatus. The rats lived in a small internal room, with one door (closed) and no window. An automatic timer turned on two fluorescent ceiling fixtures at 1900 daily; they were turned off at approximately 0700. A heater was turned on by a thermostat when the room temperature fell to 65° F; no attempt was made to control humidity. A continuous, 24-hr. record showed that the mean temperature throughout the experiment was 70.8° F with a range from 63.3° F to 75.5° F; the mean relative humidity was 50.0 per cent with a range from 39.5 per cent to 62.8 per cent.

Each animal lived separately in an 11-in. by 8-in. by 8-in. wire-mesh open-bottom cage resting on a wire-mesh grating mounted on a metal rack. A paper-lined tray under each cage caught feces and food particles that fell through the mesh. No attempt was made to control coprophagia.

Measurements. Weighed rations of food, greater than the amount the animal could eat, were placed in each cage at the beginning of the period. At the end of the period, the food remaining was taken from the cages. Food particles were carefully collected from the trays, dried, and added to the food taken from the cages, and the whole then weighed. The difference between the initial amount and the amount recovered was taken as the measure of food eaten. The error of measurement in this operation was approximately .05 gm.

An inverted, rubber-stoppered, 250-cc. chemical graduate was mounted on the side of each cage. A short length of copper tubing led from the stopper through the side of the cage. The amount of water, to the nearest .5 cc., removed by the animal was determined by reading changes of water level from the calibrated graduate. A water bottle fitted to an empty cage yielded corrections for losses due to dripping and evaporation. This measure was converted into grams.

The experimental diet consisted of dry Purina Laboratory Chow biscuits and tap water. A small piece of fresh lettuce was given daily during the free-feeding period as a dietary supplement.

Preliminary handling. For 17 days prior to the beginning of the experiment, the animals were kept on a 24-hr. feeding schedule. At 2200 daily, they were given food and water. At

2000 on the following day, food and water were withdrawn.

Daily schedules. The experiment was performed in 12 experimental periods of six days each. The first five days of each period were experimental ones; the sixth was a recovery day, during which the animals had unrestricted access to food and water. Each experimental day began at 2200. From 2200 to 1900 of the following day the animals underwent a 21-hr. *deprivation period.* At 1900, food and water ingestion through this period were measured. Then followed a *measurement period* extending from 1930 to 2030. At 2030, food and water ingestion were again measured. At 2045 all animals were given free access to food (including the lettuce) and water, and the trays were changed. Shortly before 2200, food and water were removed and clean trays placed under the cages. The deprivation period of the new experimental day began at 2200, when the experimental rations were given. Each day, then, incorporated a 21-hr. deprivation period, a second deprivation period of ½ hr., and a 1-hr. measurement period. The remaining time was devoted to experimental routine and to free feeding and drinking.

On the fifth experimental day of each of the 12 experimental periods, from 2200 to 2130 of the next calendar day, all animals had free access to both food and water. Food and water were then removed, and at 2200 the new experimental period began.

Experimental treatments. Through all five deprivation periods of each experimental period, any of four different treatments could obtain. The rat might be given: (*a*) food and water (FW), (*b*) food but no water (F), (*c*) water but no food (W), (*d*) neither food nor water (0). These, together with the immediately following ½-hr. period with neither food nor water, establish four deprivation conditions: (*a*) FW—½-hr. food deprivation, ½-hr. water deprivation; (*b*) F—½-hr. food deprivation, 21 ½-hr. water deprivation; (*c*) W—21 ½-hr. food deprivation, ½-hr. water deprivation; (*d*) 0—21 ½-hr. food deprivation, 21 ½-hr. water deprivation.

During the 1-hr. measurement period the animals could be given (*a*) both food and water (fw), (*b*) food but no water (f), (*c*) water but no food (w).[3]

---

[3] In specifying the experimental treatments, the notation introduced above will be followed throughout. When we refer to the *amounts* of food eaten, or water drunk, at any stage of the treatment, this notation will be extended by the use of italics. Thus FW*f* refers to the treatment, whereas FW*fw* refers to the quantity of water drunk during the 1-hr. period when food is present, following a ½-hr. period of deprivation of both food and water.

Measurements of both food and water ingestion were made at the end of both deprivation and measurement periods.

If we take all combinations of the two periods there are 12 different experimental treatments of deprivation and measurement. Each rat underwent all 12. The order in which any one animal went through them was determined by picking cards from a hat. The experiment was performed through the period February 8 to April 21, 1951.

RESULTS

Means of both food and water ingestion were computed for each treatment for the first two and for the last three days. Despite a slight tendency for intakes to be lower on the last three days, no significant differences appeared. For this reason, the data presented are the arithmetic means,[4] for each rat, of daily food and water intake over all five days of each experimental period.

Deprivation period. Table 1 presents the number of grams of food (1a) and water (1b) ingested by the animals during each of the three kinds of deprivation periods, subdivided according to the associated measurement periods. In Table 1 two-tailed matched t tests of the differences show that the differences between columns are significant at better than the .001 level in all cases, and that the differences within columns are not significant except for the greatest difference in the right-hand column of Table 1a, which falls between the .02 and .05 levels of probability; this may be expected by chance when 24 comparisons are made. Ingestion during the deprivation period did not depend on the measurement period of the preceding day. The data in each column were therefore lumped. In the 21-hr. period, the animals ingested approximately 51 gm. of substance when both food and water were available, 39 per cent of which was dry Purina Chow. This may be compared with Strominger's 33 per cent (20).

When food-deprived, the rats drank .41 as much as when food was available, and when water-deprived, they ate .57 of their normal intake. These numbers are the W/FW and F/FW ratios, respectively. Under these conditions the foodless animal limits its intake of water,

[4] A log transform was not found to be necessary.

TABLE 1

Experiment I

Food and Water Consumption during
Deprivation Periods

(a) Food Consumption (gms.) during 21-hour Deprivation Periods as a Function of Associated Measurement Period*

ASSOCIATED MEASUREMENT PERIOD	DEPRIVATION PERIOD				F/FW
	F		FW		
	Mean	SD	Mean	SD	
f	11.81	1.83	20.34	2.54	.58
w	10.83	1.40	20.39	2.56	.53
fw	10.75	1.65	18.27	3.40	.59
Mean	11.13	1.63	19.66	2.86	.57

(b) Water Consumption (gms.) during 21-hour Deprivation Periods as a Function of Associated Measurement Period*

ASSOCIATED MEASUREMENT PERIOD	DEPRIVATION PERIOD				W/FW
	W		FW		
	Mean	SD	Mean	SD	
f	14.61	5.86	31.71	4.10	.44
w	12.92	5.96	32.97	7.05	.39
fw	11.29	5.38	29.22	5.00	.39
Mean	12.94	5.74	31.30	5.52	.41

* Per cell, 5 observations on each of 12 animals.

and the waterless animal reduces the amount of food it eats. Water consumption is reduced more in this way than is food consumption.

Measurement period. Tables 2a and 2b present, respectively, the amounts of food and water taken during the 1-hr. measurement periods, together with their standard deviations, and the f/fw, and w/fw ratios. Matched *t* tests have been made of the difference between each mean and every other mean of each table.

In Table 2a all differences are significant at better

TABLE 2

Experiment I

Food and Water Consumption during
Measurement Periods

(a) Food Consumption (gms.) during 1-hour Measurement Periods as a Function of Preceding
Deprivation Period*

AVAILABLE DURING FIRST 21 HR. OF PRECEDING 21½ HR. (DEPRIVATION PERIOD)	FOOD CONSUMED (GMS.) WHEN ONLY FOOD AVAILABLE (f)		FOOD CONSUMED (GMS.) WHEN FOOD AND WATER BOTH AVAILABLE (fw)		RATIO (f/fw)
	Mean	SD	Mean	SD	
Nothing (0)	6.03	0.89	8.97	0.96	.67
Water (W)	7.02	1.05	8.68	1.02	.81
Food and water (FW)	2.52	1.05	3.60	1.22	.70
Food (F)	1.11	0.50	5.55	0.88	.20 (F/FW = .57)

(b) Water Consumption (gms.) during 1-hour Measurement Periods as a Function of Preceding
Deprivation Period*

AVAILABLE DURING FIRST 21 HR. OF PRECEDING 21½ HR. (DEPRIVATION PERIOD)	WATER CONSUMED (GMS.) WHEN ONLY WATER AVAILABLE (w)		WATER CONSUMED (GMS.) WHEN FOOD AND WATER BOTH AVAILABLE (fw)		RATIO (w/fw)
	Mean	SD	Mean	SD	
Nothing (0)	4.18	2.33	10.05	0.80	.42
Food (F)	14.00	3.45	15.85	3.14	.88
Food and water (FW)	3.20	1.37	4.77	1.35	.67
Water (W)	1.08	0.98	7.26	1.41	.15 (W/FW = .41)

* Per cell, 5 observations on each of 12 animals; SD's with respect to 12 submeans.

than the .01 level, except three: (*a*) FW*f* and FW*fw* differ between the .02 and .05 levels of significance; this *f*/*fw* ratio, however, is in conformity with ratios obtained over the 22 hr. of the ingestion period. (*b*) No significant difference appears between W*fw* and 0*fw*. Whether or not water is available during food deprivation makes little difference in the amount eaten at the end of the period *provided* it is available when the food is given. (*c*) F*fw* and 0*f* do not differ significantly. Rats that have been deprived only of water eat just as much food when water is given to them as do rats first deprived of both food and water and then given food without water.

In Table 2*b* all differences are significant at better than the .01 level except as follows: (*a*) Between F*w* and F*fw*; water-deprived rats drink large quantities of water irrespective of the presence of food when water is given them. The *w*/*fw* ratio deviates from 1.00 in the direction expected from the deprivation period. (*b*) Between 0*w* and FW*fw*, and 0*w* and FW*w*. The rat first deprived of both food and water, and then given water, drinks no more than an effectively satiated animal. A strong "hunger drive" seems to suppress drinking and might be said to "inhibit thirst."

The "self-imposed" deprivation reveals itself in the *w*/*fw* and *f*/*fw* ratios. The ratio reaches its maximum when, for 22½ hr., the animals have been deprived of the substance measured, and its minimum when the animals have been deprived of the other substance.

Food and water intakes are thus a function not solely of food and water deprivation, respectively, but of both these and of the substances available at the time of measurement. Speaking loosely, thirsty rats are hungry rats and vice versa, and the simple failure of S to take either food or water offered alone after the animal has been satiated with it, will predict not at all what S will do if presented with food and water together.

During the deprivation period, a food-deprived animal cuts down its water intake and effectively becomes water-deprived as well. Similarly, a water-deprived animal cuts down its food intake and becomes food-deprived. The present data show that effects of these self-imposed deprivations appear when measurements are made of food and water intake together in the hour following termination of deprivation.

We have performed two further experiments. In the first, we deprived the animals of water for 21½ hr., then for 1 hr. made different combinations of food and water available to various groups of animals. In the hour following this, we measured food intake. In the second study, a parallel procedure has been followed with food deprivation.

EXPERIMENT II

In the second experiment we deprived the animals of water for 21 hr., leaving food available (F); then allowed free access, either to food and water (fw′), to food only (f′), water only (w′), or nothing (0′), for 1 hr.; and in the following period of 1 hr. (f) measured the amount of food eaten in the absence of water. These procedures define a *deprivation period*, an *ingestion period*, and a *measurement period*.

METHOD

The second experiment was run through five days. The 12 Ss, the apparatus, and basic method were the same as those used in the first experiment. At the time this experiment began, Ss ranged from 201 to 204 days in age. The daily schedule was as follows: At 2200 all animals were given unlimited food but no water (f). At 1900 of the following day, 3 randomly assigned animals were given food and water (Group fw′), 3 were given food but no water (Group f′), 3 were given water but no food (Group w′), and 3 were deprived of both food and water (Group 0′). All food and water were removed at 2000, and at 2010 all animals were given a measured amount of food but no water (f). At 2110 all food was removed; the amount eaten was measured. At 2127 all animals were given access to food and water with supplementary lettuce. Water was removed at 2200, the beginning of the new experimental period.

RESULTS

Table 3a presents for the four groups of animals the means and standard deviations of the quantities of food eaten in the 1-hr. measurement period. Significance of differences was determined by t tests. Since the preceding experiment led us to expect particular differences, these t tests were one-tailed. The amount of food eaten

TABLE 3

(a) Experiment II

Food Consumption (gms.) during 1-hour Measurement
Periods Following Various Combinations of 21-hour
Water-Deprivation Period (F) and 1-hour
Ingestion Periods

(each cell, 5 days' observation on each of 3 animals)

AVAILABLE IN 22-HR. DEPRIVATION PERIOD	AVAILABLE IN 1-HR. INGESTION PERIOD	GMS. FOOD EATEN IN 1-HR. MEASUREMENT PERIOD	
		Mean	SD
F	water (w')	6.02	0.76
F	food and water (fw')	2.95	0.64
F	food (f')	1.11	0.33
F	nothing (0')	1.61	0.97

(b) Experiment III

Water Consumption (gms.) during 1-hour Measurement
Periods Following Various Combinations of 21-hour
Food-Deprivation Period (W) and 1-hour
Ingestion Periods

(each cell, 48 animals)

AVAILABLE IN 21-HR. DEPRIVATION PERIOD	AVAILABLE IN 1-HR. INGESTION PERIOD	GMS. WATER DRUNK IN 1-HR. MEASUREMENT PERIOD (1st 5 days)		GMS. WATER DRUNK IN 1-HR. MEASUREMENT PERIOD (25 days)	
		Mean	SD	Mean	SD
W	water (w')	1.2	0.7	1.4	1.5
W	food and water (fw')	3.2	1.0	3.8	2.0
W	food (f')	10.5	1.9	10.6	2.6
W	nothing (0')	1.3	0.8	1.4	1.4

by the first group (w') is significantly different, at the
.01 level, from that eaten by any of the other groups.
Group fw' differs, as well, from Group f at the .02 level.
Other differences, although not statistically significant,
fall in the appropriate direction and are of the appropriate

magnitudes. No effects of age, or of the sampling procedure, are evident.

The eating behavior of these animals is in remarkable quantitative agreement with the behavior under analogous conditions summarized in Table 2. The data conform with the predictions based on the results of the preceding experiment.

EXPERIMENT III

In the third experiment,[5] we deprived the animals of food for 21 hr. (W); then allowed them free access either to food and water (fw'), to food only (f'), to water only (w'), or to nothing (0') for 1 hr.; and in the following period of 1 hr. measured the amount of water drunk in the absence of food. These procedures again define a *deprivation period*, an *ingestion* period, and a *Measurement period*.

METHOD

Subjects. The Ss were 48 male albino rats, run in three squads. The first squad contained 16 animals of the Hisaw strain, 119 days old at the beginning of the experiment. The second and third squads were both of the Wistar strain, aged 98 and 127 days, respectively, at the beginning of the measurements.

Experimental room and apparatus. Throughout the experiment the rats were housed in a small internal room with one door and no windows. Two fluorescent ceiling fixtures came on at 0530 daily and turned off at 1730. A coil-type heater fan, blowing over an open vessel of water, was turned on by a thermostat. Temperatures measured at the beginning of the daily experimental sessions averaged 71.7° F, ± 3.0°, and the relative humidity averaged 67.6 per cent, ± 5.0 per cent. The cages, food, water graduates, and tubes were the same as those used in Experiment I.

Measurements. Drinking was measured with the same apparatus and methods as in Experiment I. In this experiment, however, reading accuracy was to the nearest 1 cc.

Preliminary handling. For 8 days the animals were housed in the room and stabilized on the temperature and light-dark cycle with free access to food and water. For the next 15 days

---

[5] The data of Experiment III were collected by Mr. Ogden R. Lindsley in the course of another experiment performed with the senior author.

the rats had free access to water, but access to food for only 1 hr. per day.

Daily schedules. The experiment proper ran for 25 days. Each day included the following operations: At 0530 the lights went on. At 1300 temperature and humidity were measured and the rats weighed. Water was next removed from pairs of cages at 6-min. intervals, and the experimental diet of the 1-hr. ingestion period was correspondingly given to the animals, according to their group memberships. General procedures otherwise conformed with those followed in the preceding experiment. The staggering was necessary because these measurements were made in the course of another experiment.

Summarizing, each animal was submitted to a *deprivation period*, 20 hr. and 50 min. in length, with access to water but no food (W). During the next hour, the *ingestion period*, the experimental groups received differential treatment. Following this, after a short delay, came a 1-hr. *measurement period*, when water alone was available. At the end of this time, each animal was given access to food for 1 hr., in addition to the water, and the experimental day was over.

Groups. Four of the 16 animals of each squad were randomly assigned to one or another of four groups, which differed in the diet given during the ingestion period. Group fw′ received food and water, Group f′ food without water, Group w′ only water, and Group 0′ received nothing.

The experiment was run through the period November, 1951 to April, 1952.

RESULTS

No significant differences appeared in the drinking of rats of the Hisaw and of the Wistar strains. The data of all the animals under each treatment were therefore lumped and treated together.

Table 3b presents the data obtained during the first 5 days and through the whole 25 days of the experiment. One-tailed *t* tests of significance were made. Over the first five days, Group f′ differed significantly, at better than the .001 level, from Group fw′. Group fw′ differed at the .06 level from Group 0′. Over the full 25 days, all three groups differed from one another at better than the .001 level. Through neither period did Groups 0′ and w′ differ significantly from one another.

The results are in substantial quantitative agreement with those reported in Table 2. Group f′ is effectively rendered thirsty (as evidenced by drinking behavior) by the termination of the 22-hr. period of food deprivation.

The results of all three experiments are in good agreement. Food and water intake of the white rat are interdependent to a high degree. Experimental deprivation of one is associated with a large drop in the intake of the other that may be considered a "self-imposed" deprivation. At the termination of an experimental deprivation period, the rat's tendencies to eat are almost independent of whether it was deprived of food or of water.

These results confirm and extend findings already available in the literature we have cited. More important, they clarify the quantitative relationships involved.

There is reason to expect that noningestive habits acquired under food and water deprivation will behave much as do eating and drinking (7, 18, 19). More pertinently, Kendler (10) has observed a depression of food-conditioned responses when the animal is deprived of water as well as of food for 22½ hr., and he has found, too, that food- and water-deprived animals learn a simple T maze more slowly than animals that have been deprived of food alone. Webb (22) has also presented data showing that water deprivation controls habits that have been rewarded by food.

On the other hand, Miller, Bailey, and Stevenson (12) found that animals that have been subjected to operative techniques involving the hypothalamus may show a considerable dissociation between amounts of food eaten and the strength of behavior acquired under food deprivation with reinforcement by food.

The large size of the interaction effects we have found and the lack of strict reciprocity between food and water intakes after long periods of deprivation suggest reasons for the anomalous results in experiments on "latent learning" (6). The logical controversy over the behavior of "thirsty" and "hungry" animals loses much of its force when the assumptions that have been made, implicitly or explicitly, about the behavior of "hungry" rats toward water and of "thirsty" rats toward food prove unjustified.

That "low motivation" may be a condition necessary for the exhibition of certain classes of behavior may follow from our results on simple eating and drinking.

Simple formulations of "drive" and "drive summation" such as those that have been made on the basis of Hull's 1943 theoretical treatment (9) seem to require revision. Perhaps new classes of "drives"—"latent drives" or "concomitant drives"—need to be introduced. Perhaps it will be more fruitful if these endeavors are held in abeyance until further experimentation clarifies the phenomena associated with deprivation.

Several physiological mechanisms may account for these results. Perhaps a thirsty rat cannot very efficiently eat dry food such as we used. Probably more important is the role of water in the digestive and metabolic processes (3). It is not clear, however, that the physiologists are yet in a position to give us a reasonably coherent description of the processes involved.

Further experimentation will probably have two merits: it should enable us to specify the conditions of deprivation and reinforcement associated with efficient learning, and it should provide the data which seem to us indispensible for further production of theories of drive or of latent learning.

SUMMARY AND CONCLUSIONS

Three experiments were performed on the effects of food and water deprivation on the albino rat's ingestion of food and water. In the first, the Ss were placed on various schedules that deprived them of food, or of water, or of both food and water, or of neither, for 22 hr. After a further ½ hr. of deprivation of both, they were given food, or water, or both. Through all periods the amounts of each substance ingested were measured. Two further experiments tested hypotheses derived from the results of the first. In one, animals were deprived of water for 22 hr., and then various groups were given 1 hr. of food, or water, neither food nor water, or both. In the following hour, they were again given food, and the quantity eaten in 1 hr. was measured. In the other, a parallel design deprived the animals of food for 22 hr., then each of four groups received food, water, neither, or both for 1 hr. They were then given access to water for 1 hr., and the amount drunk was measured. From the results of these experiments, the following conclusions are drawn:

1. The amount of food eaten by water-deprived rats is some 60 per cent of the amount eaten by those which are *not* water-deprived.

2. The amount of water drunk by food-deprived rats is some 40 per cent of the amount drunk by those which are *not* food-deprived.

3. If a 21-hr. period of water deprivation is terminated, the amount of food eaten rises to some 6 gm., which approaches the amount of food eaten after a like period of food deprivation.

4. If a 21-hr. period of food deprivation is terminated, the amount of water drunk rises to some $7/10$ cc., which approaches the amount of water drunk after a like period of water deprivation.

5. These increases in water and food intake are of the same order of magnitude, whether the measurement is made at the time the experimental deprivation periods are being terminated by eating or drinking, or in the period following such termination.

6. Considerable questions are raised by these results for some current treatments of "drive" and for the interpretation, in terms of so-called "irrelevant drive" and "high" and "low" motivation, of the results of latent-learning experiments involving the behavior of food- and water-deprived rats.

REFERENCES

1. ADOLPH, E. F. *Physiological regulations.* Lancaster, Pa.: Cattell, 1943.
2. BOUSFIELD, W. A., & ELLIOTT, M. H. The effect of fasting on the eating behavior of rats. *J. genet. Psychol.*, 1934, 45, 227-237.
3. BROBECK, J. Regulation of energy exchange. *Ann. Rev. Physiol.*, 1948, 10, 315-328.
4. FINGER,, F. W., & REID, L. S. The effect of water depriva-

tion and subsequent satiation upon general activity in the rat. *J. comp. physiol. Psychol.*, 1952, 45, 368-372.

5. GREGERSON, M. I. Studies on the regulation of water intake. II. Conditions affecting the daily water intake of dogs as registered continuously by a potometer. *Amer. J. Physiol.*, 1932, 102, 344-349.

6. HAYES, K. J. An experimental criticism of the Spence and Lippitt procedure. *Amer. Psychologist*, 1949, 4, 223. (Abstract)

7. HORENSTEIN, BETTY R. Performance of conditioned responses as a function of strength of hunger drive. *J. comp. physiol. Psychol.*, 1951, 44, 10-224.

8. HULL, C. L. Differential ation to internal stimuli in the albino rat. *J. comp. ol.*, 1933, 16, 255-273.

9. HULL, C. L. *Principles of behavior.* New York: Appleton-Century, 1943.

10. KENDLER, H. H. Drive interaction: 1. Learning as a function of the simultaneous presence of the hunger and thirst drives. *J. exp. Psychol.*, 1945, 35, 96-109.

11. KLEITMAN, N. The effect of starvation on the daily consumption of water by the dog. *Amer. J. Physiol.*, 1927, 81, 336-340.

12. MILLER, N., BAILEY, C. J., & STEVENSON, J. A. F. Decreased "hunger" but increased food intake resulting from hypothalamic lesions. *Science*, 1950, 112, 256-259.

13. PERNICE, B., & SCAGLIOSI, G. Ueber die Wirkung der Wasserentziehung auf Thiere. *Arch. Path. Anat.*, 1895, 139, 155-184.

14. ROBINSON, E. A., & ADOLPH, E. F. Pattern of normal water drinking in dogs. *Amer. J. Physiol.*, 1943, 139, 39-44.

15. SIEGEL, P. S. The relationship between voluntary water intake, body weight, and number of hours of water deprivation in the rat. *J. comp. physiol. Psychol.*, 1947, 40, 231-238.

16. SIEGEL, P. S., & STUCKEY, H. L. An examination of some factors relating to the voluntary water intake of the rat. *J. comp. physiol. Psychol.*, 1947, 40, 271-274.

17. SIEGEL, P. S., & TALANTIS, B. S. Water intake as a function of privation interval when food is withheld. *J. comp. physiol. Psychol.*, 1950, 43, 62-65.

18. SKINNER, B. F. Drive and reflex strength. *J. gen. Psychol.*, 1932, 6, 22-37.

19. SKINNER, B. F. Drive and reflex strength: II. *J. gen. Psychol.*, 1932, 6, 38-48.

20. STROMINGER, J. L. The relation between water intake and

food intake in normal rats and rats with hypothalamic
hyperphagia. *Yale J. biol. Med.*, 1947, 19, 279-288.

21. THISTLETHWAITE, D. A critical review of latent learning
and related experiments. *Psychol. Bull.*, 1951, 48, 97-129.

22. WEBB, W. B. The motivational aspect of an irrelevant
drive in the behavior of the white rat. *J. exp. Psychol.*,
1949, 39, 1-14.

Part III

The Effects of Drive on Learning and Performance

13

Behavior Potentiality as a Joint Function of the Amount of Training and the Degree of Hunger at the Time of Extinction[1]

C. THEODORE PERIN

Department of Psychology, Institute of Human Relations, Yale University

The following selection presents the combined findings of Perin and Williams concerning the factors responsible for the performance of a response during extinction, that is, when reinforcement no longer follows the performance of the conditioned response. These investigators show that extinction responding is a joint function of the drive level during extinction and the number of reinforced responses during acquisition.

The article is reprinted from the Journal of Experimental Psychology, 1942, 30, 93-113, *with the permission of the author and the American Psychological Association.*

For the most part, experiments designed to show relations between observed behavior and conditions antecedent to the occurrence of the behavior have been

[1] This investigation is a part of the coordinated research program of the Institute of Human Relations, Yale University. The writer is greatly indebted to Professor Clark L. Hull, under whose direction the experiment was carried out, for valuable suggestions and criticisms. A number of intricate curve-fitting problems were solved by Mr. Bengt Carlson. The results of an earlier study by Dr. S. B. Williams are reproduced here with his kind permission. The experimental results of this study were contained in a thesis presented by the writer in partial fulfillment of the requirements for the degree of Master of Arts, Yale University, 1940.

limited to single pairs of variables. In such experiments all known antecedent variables except one are held as constant as experimental conditions will permit. This one variable, sometimes called the experimental variable, is varied systematically by the experimenter, and the concomitant changes in the dependent or consequent variable are noted. Nearly all animal-drive studies have been carried out in the fashion just described.

Crutchfield (1) has pointed out that generalizations are extremely limited when only a single antecedent variable is used, and that investigation of the interaction of antecedent variables in the determination of behavior is impossible when only one antecedent variable is present in any given experiment. Fitts (5) also has recognized the importance, as well as the difficulties, of experiments involving more than one antecedent variable.

The present study is a multi-variable one in that it is designed to show behavior as a mathematical function of two antecedent variables, the degree of training, and the intensity of the hunger drive present at the time the behavior potential is measured. The approach to the multi-variable problem here employed is distinctly different from the Fisher design which Crutchfield has advocated.[2] Basically the present design is of three-dimensional form with the two experimental variables occupying two of the dimensions, and the measure of behavior potentiality occupying the third dimension.[3] With the

---

[2] Unfortunately, the Fisher procedure yields merely an indication of the degree of dependence of some consequent variable upon a number of antecedent variables, and gives no indication of the nature of the functional relationships involved. For rather gross practical purposes, such as are characteristic of agriculture, the extent of the relationship among variables regardless of their functional nature may be sufficient, but for a science which hopes for precise systematization the determination of joint functional relationships is indispensable. For that reason the Fisher design type of experiment with its characteristic economies of time and effort was rejected in the present investigation in favor of a far more laborious experimental procedure which would permit accurate determination of these joint functional relationships.

[3] Williams (11) has applied the 3-dimensional design to an experimental situation and has pointed out the advantages of this design from the standpoint of methodology.

data presented in this manner it is possible to express a measure of behavior potentiality as a function of either of the antecedent or experimental variables taken singly (the other remaining constant) or of both antecedent variables acting together.

The term *behavior potentiality* is used here with specific reference to the way in which the behavior is measured. For example, when an albino rat has been trained to press a lever in order to obtain a pellet of food and the hungry animal is then given access to the lever but no food is given when the lever is pressed, the lever-pressing response may be expected to cease after a number of responses have been made. When the non-reinforced responses are counted, the result may be taken as an indication of the response potentiality before the response was extinguished. The potentiality, then, can be measured only after it has ceased to be a potentiality and has become an actuality through occurrence.

SUBJECTS AND APPARATUS

The subjects for this experiment were 320 male albino rats approximately 90 days old and ranging from 180 to 225 grams in weight.

The apparatus consisted of four modified Skinner boxes of the type used by Ellson (2) and Williams (10). These boxes were partially soundproofed and were ventilated by means of the laboratory suction line. The compartment in which the animal was placed measured one foot along each of its three dimensions. At one end of the cubical compartment was a brass panel and through an aperture in this panel a horizontal bar 55 mm in length could be inserted in the box (Fig. 1). The aperture was automatically covered by a sliding shutter when the bar was withdrawn. During the training period, pressure of fifteen grams on the bar by the rat closed a mercury-cup contact in series with an electromagnetic food release. The resulting action of the magnet released one pellet of food from the food magazine into the food tray. In addition, pressure on the bar activated a magnetic signal marker mounted on a constant-speed, waxed-paper polygraph, thus recording the number of responses and the time required for each response. The pellets were made from a mixture of finely ground calf meal and water. The mixture was molded into a cylindrical shape and after drying it was cut into small cylinders weighing about .05 gram

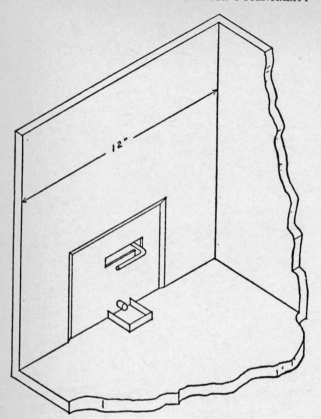

Fig. 1. *Showing the interior of the experimental compartment with the horizontal bar inserted in position for pressing. Beneath the bar is the end of the glass tube through which pellets of food are delivered into the food tray.*

each. The consumption of one pellet thus secured constituted one reinforcement. During extinction of the habit, the food release mechanism was disconnected, though the connection between the bar and the polygraph marker was retained so that the animal's reactions were still recorded. Drinking water was always available to the animal in the box.

PROCEDURE

Data were obtained from 40 rats in each of eight different subgroups employed. For convenience in experimentation and exposition, the animals were divided into two groups (A and B), and each of these main groups was in turn divided into four subgroups.

The two experimental variables selected for systematic investigation were: (1) the number of reinforced responses the animals were permitted to make during the learning period, and (2) the degree of hunger at the time the habit underwent extinction, the hunger being measured by the number of hours' time since the animal was satiated. These two antecedent variables are shown in Fig. 2. Actually the two main groups may be

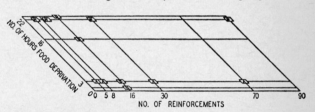

Fig. 2. Showing the different combinations of the two antecedent variables. The subgroups of Group A are represented by the letter A, those for Group B and the Williams experiment by the letters B and W respectively.

considered to make up two different experiments. Group A represents the animals which were used to determine the strength of the habit at the time of extinction as a function of the number of reinforced responses the animals were given during the learning. All of the animals in this group were extinguished with the same degree of hunger. Group B, on the other hand, represents animals which were all given the same number of reinforcements during learning but which were extinguished under different amounts of hunger. Thus Group B determines the strength of the bar-pressing response as a function of the degree of hunger at the time of extinction. By a fortunate circumstance, Williams (10) had already studied the extinction behavior of large groups of rats under conditions such that their results could be combined effectively with those of Groups A and B of the present experiment; we shall call the Williams animals Group W.

Figure 2 presents diagrammatically the subgroups of A, B, and W in relation to each of the two antecedent variables. A more precise numerical statement is given in Table 1. A study of Figure 2 will show that Groups A and W are alike in that

TABLE 1

SUMMARY OF PROCEDURES FOR GROUPS A AND B AS WELL AS THE
PROCEDURE FOR THE WILLIAMS EXPERIMENT

All learning was performed under 23 hours' food privation.

Subgroup	Number of Animals	Number of Reinforcements on Learning Day	Number of Hours' Hunger on Extinction Day
Group A			
1	40	5	3
2	40	8	3
3	40	30	3
4	40	70	3
Group B			
5	40	16	1
6	40	16	3
7	40	16	16
8	40	16	23
Williams' experiment			
1	35	5	22
2	35	10	22
3	35	30	22
4	35	90	22

the number of repetitions was varied systematically, whereas extinction occurred under a constant number of hours of food deprivation in each (3 hours in Group A and 22 hours in Group W). In Group B, on the other hand, the number of hours of food deprivation was varied systematically while the number of reinforcements was kept constant at 16. Thus Group B, having one subgroup in common with Group A and one subgroup almost in common with Group W, constitutes a relational connecting link between the other two groups.

The general procedure involved in feeding the animals, habituating them to the experimental boxes, and training them to secure pellets by pressing the horizontal bar followed closely the precedent set by the experiments of Ellson (2) and Williams (10). Each animal was fed moist food for one-half hour daily for one week. The moist food was made by mixing a small amount of water with dry, finely ground calf meal to form a mash. In order to establish a definite feeding rhythm and to facilitate a more rapid satiation preceding extinction, this feeding occurred at the same time of day that the rat would later be trained and subsequently extinguished. Following this the animals were fed in the experimental compartments for two days, one-half hour each day, the food in this case being dry pellets which were readily accessible in the food tray of the box.

The experimental period proper consisted of three separate sub-divisions: (1) habituation to securing food in the food cup at the click of the food-release mechanism; (2) training on the bar-pressing habit; (3) extinction of the learned habit.

Habituation.—In the habituation to the click of the food mechanism, the animals were given 40 pellets one at a time, the food release being operated by the experimenter through the manipulation of a switch mounted on top of the experimental box. In this procedure, 3 pellets were present in the food tray when the rat was first placed in the box. As the third pellet was being eaten, another pellet was released into the food tray and the remaining pellets were given one at a time just after the previous pellet had been completely consumed. This procedure served to prevent the rats from becoming frightened at the sound of the food mechanism, and the habit was set up whereby the animals obtained and ate a pellet immediately following each click of the mechanism. After the animals had been given 20 pellets in this manner they were returned to the living cages for 15 minutes, after which they were again put in the experimental boxes and given another 20 pellets in the same way.

Training.—The day following habituation to the boxes and to the food-delivery device, the animals were trained on the bar-pressing response. A small amount of moist food was placed on the brass panel immediately above the horizontal bar. In attempting to remove the moist food the animals pressed the bar accidentally and a food pellet was released into the tray. Usually three or four pellets were obtained in this 'accidental' fashion, and the first reinforced response was counted when the bar was pressed and the pellet eaten immediately after delivery.[4] The animals of the different subgroups were given the required number of pellet-reinforced responses in this manner, and were then returned to the living cages. When the data are examined for consistency within a subgroup and between subgroups for the time required to secure the first five pellets, the above procedure appears satisfactory (Table 2).[5]

[4] Animals engaged in removing moist food from the panel often did not find the pellets released by 'accidental' pressure on the bar until after a number of seconds had passed. The experimenter watched each animal closely in order to count as the first reinforcement that bar response which was followed immediately by the rat's eating of the pellet.

[5] Since one subgroup was allowed to make only 5 reinforced responses, the learning ability of all subgroups was compared on the basis of the first 5 reinforcements.

A half hour after each rat had been returned to its living cage it was given the amount of dry food necessary to raise the total quantity eaten to 70 pellets for the session.

Extinction.—Since different subgroups of rats were to be extinguished with different degrees of hunger drive as measured

TABLE 2

TABLE SHOWING EQUIVALENCE OF LEARNING ABILITY FOR
THE VARIOUS EXPERIMENTAL SUBGROUPS

Group A		Subgroup Number			
		1	2	3	4
Time needed to secure first 5 pellets (minutes)	Mean	2.31	2.40	2.10	2.21
	Median	2.20	2.10	1.85	1.85
	$\sigma_{mdn.}$	.21	.21	.16	.21
Group B		5	6	7	8
Time needed to secure first 5 pellets (minutes)	Mean	2.37	2.15	2.24	2.32
	Median	2.20	1.95	2.10	2.00
	$\sigma_{mdn.}$	.28	.19	.19	.21

by the number of hours of food deprivation, it was necessary to have all of the animals satiated to the same degree at the beginning of the privation period. Moist food was placed in the living cage one hour before the time from which drive was to be measured. Near the end of the one-hour satiation period each animal was fed by hand, both moist and dry food being presented. When an animal would no longer eat either the moist or the dry food even upon repeated presentations, the food was removed and the time noted in order to determine the hour at which the animal should be extinguished with the proper period of food deprivation.

An arbitrary criterion of extinction was used, the bar responses being considered extinguished when a 5-minute period had elapsed during which no responses were made. Three measures of behavior potentiality were used. These were: (1) the number of extinction (non-rewarded) responses before the 5-minute criterion of no response; (2) the time required for extinction, exclusive of the 5-minute criterion; (3) the latency or time required to make the first 3 extinction responses, a single latency being the temporal interval between the point in time at which an animal was placed in the experimental compartment and that at which it pushed the bar.

The time required to make the first response of the extinction series is the only latency measure not influenced by the extinction effect resulting from preceding non-rewarded trials, but in the present experiment three separate latencies were obtained from each animal at the beginning of the extinction period in order to insure more reliable latencies by means of larger sampling. The three latencies were separated by one-minute recovery intervals during which the animal was removed from the experimental box; these recovery intervals were introduced in the hope of eliminating, through spontaneous recovery, the major part of the extinction effects resulting from the preceding non-reinforcements. After the third latency response had been made, each animal was left in the experimental box until the criterion of 5 minutes with no response was reached.

During the extinction trials the food mechanism was disconnected and thus there was no characteristic click when the bar responses were made.

RESULTS

A preliminary picture of the nature of the present experimental results is yielded by the data distributions for resistance to experimental extinction as a function of reinforcements (food privation constant at 3 hours) as presented in Fig. 3. There it may be seen that the ani-

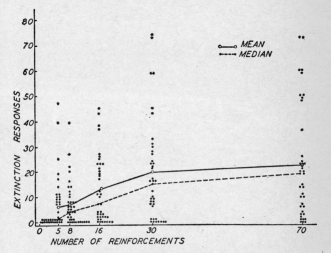

Fig. 3. Showing the distribution of the number of extinction responses of individual animals within the various subgroups for Group A. The solid line connects the means of the distributions and the dashed line shows the trend of the medians as reinforcement increases.

mals of the several subgroups, even with both motivation and number of reinforcements constant, varied considerably in their behavior potentiality. It is also apparent that all five of the distributions show a marked tendency to concentration at the zero extreme, this tendency being especially marked where the number of reinforcements is small. Finally, it is to be observed that the median values in all cases fall markedly below the means, exactly as is to be expected from the skewed nature of the distributions. This marked skewness is characteristic of the other measures of behavior potentiality in Groups A, B, and W, and for this reason the median values have been selected as the basis for comparison of the various subgroups and in the later determinations of behavior potentiality in its functional relations with the antecedent variables, reinforcement and drive.

BEHAVIOR POTENTIALITY—GROUP A

The numerical results of all three measures of behavior potential for all subgroups of Group A are given in Table 3, and the critical ratios indicating the reliabilities of the differences are given in Table 4. The results for the number of extinction responses obtained from Group A are shown graphically in Figs. 4, 6, 8, with the results for extinction time appearing in Fig. 9 and those for initial latency in Fig. 10. In general, an increase in the number of reinforcements with hunger drive constant for extinction, results in a corresponding increase in extinction responses and extinction time, with latency decreasing with increased reinforcement.

Williams (10) reports that at 22 hours' hunger drive the number of extinction responses as a function of previous reinforcement conformed to the equation,

$$N = 62 - 62 \times 10^{-.017R}, \qquad (1)$$

where N is the number of extinction responses, and R is the number of reinforced trials during acquisition. By the nature of equation (1), if R equals zero, N also equals zero, since that is the origin of the curve. The equation also indicates that the first reinforcement will yield a measurable amount of extinction response. Closer

TABLE 3

Showing the Effect of the Number of Reinforcements during Training on the Measures of Behavior Potentiality

All animals had a 3-hour hunger drive at the beginning of the extinction period. $N = 40$ in each subgroup.

		Group A			
		Number of Reinforcements			
Measure of Behavior Potentiality		5	8	30	70
(a) Extinction responses	Mean	6.50	6.80	19.40	22.70
	Median	1.00	4.00	15.50	19.00
	$\sigma_{mdn.}$	2.07	1.66	3.91	4.88
(b) Extinction time (minutes)	Mean	4.95	4.45	8.13	8.94
	Median	0.75	3.25	7.05	9.45
	$\sigma_{mdn.}$	1.40	0.96	1.36	1.22
(c) Initial latency * during extinction period (minutes)	Median	2.33	0.90	0.60	0.50
	Q	2.20	1.31	0.66	0.95

* The initial latency was determined by taking three successive latencies for each of the 40 animals in a subgroup with a one-minute period between the latencies to permit spontaneous recovery. The 120 latencies for a subgroup were then combined into a single distribution and the median for that distribution was computed. Occasionally animals made no responses within the 5 minutes which were allowed and the latencies for those cases were indeterminate, making it impossible to compute means for the distributions. Also, it was considered unwise to compute the $\sigma_{mdn.}$ directly from the distribution in the way Garrett (6) outlines because of the scarcity of cases at the medians. In addition, no $\sigma_{m.}$ was available from which the $\sigma_{mdn.}$ could be computed. For these reasons the differences between subgroups were not tested for significance with regard to initial latency. Semi-interquartile ranges (Q) are given for initial latencies as an indication of variability.

TABLE 4

Showing the Reliabilities of the Differences between the Measures* of Habit Strength. Critical Ratios (diff./$\sigma_{diff.}$) of the Medians for Paired Subgroups

	Group A	
Paired Subgroups (Number of Reinforcements)	Measures of Behavior Potentiality	
	Number of Responses	Extinction Time
5 reinf. vs. 8..........................	C.R. = 1.13	C.R. = 1.47
5 reinf. vs. 16..........................	1.82	2.11
5 reinf. vs. 30..........................	3.28	3.23
5 reinf. vs. 70..........................	3.40	4.68
8 reinf. vs. 16..........................	0.98	0.85
8 reinf. vs. 30..........................	2.71	1.66
8 reinf. vs. 70..........................	2.91	4.00
16 reinf. vs. 30..........................	1.82	1.51
16 reinf. vs. 70..........................	2.56	3.31
30 reinf. vs. 70..........................	0.56	1.31

* Critical ratios were not obtained for the initial latency measures because of the method used in securing the latencies (see footnote for Table 3).

examination of Williams' data has since revealed that these were not valid assumptions, and consequently a better fit to the Williams data has been obtained with the equation,

$$N = 66(1 - 10^{-.018R}) - 4. \qquad (2)$$

The curve obtained by substituting different R values in this equation is shown in Fig. 4. This is an exponential or growth curve which approaches 62 extinction responses, the asymptote, when the number of reinforcements becomes very large. The curve also indicates that

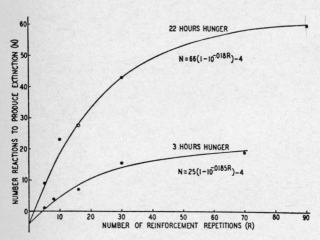

Fig. 4. Curves showing the relation of extinction responses (N) to the number of reinforcements (R) at two levels of drive. The upper curve of extinction at 22 hours' hunger is taken from Williams' experiment, while the lower curve at 3 hours' hunger represents Group A of the present experiment. The solid circles are the empirical values for the median number of extinction responses with the curves themselves being plotted by substituting different values for R in the corresponding equations. The hollow circle represents an interpolation in the equation of our Group B at h = 22 and R = 16. The close agreement of this value with Williams' results, as a whole, largely justifies the combination of the Williams data with those of the present experiment.

a minimum number of reinforced trials, in this case 1.51, must be given before the behavior potentiality becomes sufficiently large to result in an overt reaction and so in any number of extinction responses at all. The value 1.51 was determined by substituting $N = 0$ in equation (2) and solving for R. The -4 of equation (2) indicates that absolute zero lies 4 extinction units below the reaction threshold.

The same general type of equation (exponential) was fitted to the data for Group A of the present experiment, and is represented graphically as the lower curve in Fig. 4. This equation is

$$N = 25(1 - 10^{-.0185R}) - 4. \qquad (3)$$

From examination of the two curves shown in Fig. 4, it is evident that the degree of hunger plays an important role in determining the characteristics of those curves. Since the degree of hunger at the time of extinction is the only significant antecedent variable by which the two curves can be differentiated, it is evident that a change in drive changes the ultimate limit of the curve, but the origin does not change and the coefficients of R in the two equations (.018 vs. .0185) are practically identical.

Comparable curves were fitted to the data for the time necessary to produce extinction and to the initial latency values during the extinction period (Figs. 9 and 10).

BEHAVIOR POTENTIALITY—GROUP B

It is evident from a comparison of Williams' results with those from Group A (Fig. 4) that there is a marked positive relation between the drive at the time of extinction and the resistance to extinction. The animals of Group B were run primarily in order to secure quantitative statements of the nature and extent of this relationship.

The results of the three measures of behavior potentiality for Group B are given in Table 5, and the critical ratios indicating the reliabilities of the differences appear in Table 6. The results for the number of extinction responses are shown graphically in Figs. 5 and 8,

TABLE 5

SHOWING THE EFFECT OF THE DEGREE OF HUNGER AT THE TIME OF EXTINCTION
ON THE MEASURES OF BEHAVIOR POTENTIALITY

All animals had been given the same amount of training (16 reinforcements). $N = 40$ in all subgroups.

Measure of Behavior Potentiality		Group B			
		Number of Hours' Hunger			
		1	3	16	23
(a) Extinction responses	Mean	9.10	12.30	24.50	32.90
	Median	6.00	7.00	19.00	29.50
	$\sigma_{mdn.}$	2.01	2.57	4.34	4.46
(b) Extinction time (minutes)	Mean	4.61	6.24	9.76	12.84
	Median	4.45	4.45	7.65	13.75
	$\sigma_{mdn.}$	0.44	1.05	1.53	1.09
(c) Initial latency * during extinction period (minutes)	Median	0.95	0.90	0.45	0.25
	Q	1.74	1.52	0.42	0.18

* See footnote for Table 4.

with those for extinction time and initial latency appearing in Figs. 9 and 10 respectively. Equations have been fitted to the data for Group B, as in Group A. For example, when the number of reinforcements is held constant, the equation for the number of extinction responses as a function of the number of hours' hunger (h) at the time of extinction becomes

$$N = 9.4 \times 10^{.0241h} - 4. \qquad (4)$$

The curve shown in Fig. 5 indicates that even though the animals have a zero hunger drive, as measured by food deprivation, they may be expected to make a num-

TABLE 6

SHOWING THE RELIABILITIES OF THE DIFFERENCES BETWEEN THE MEASURES* OF
BEHAVIOR POTENTIALITY. CRITICAL RATIOS (diff./$\sigma_{diff.}$) OF THE
MEDIANS FOR PAIRED SUBGROUPS

Paired Subgroups (Hours of Hunger)	Group B	
	Measures of Behavior Potentiality	
	Number of Responses	Extinction Time
1 hour vs. 3	C.R. = 0.31	C.R. = 0.00
1 hour vs. 16	2.72	2.01
1 hour vs. 23	4.81	7.88
3 hours vs. 16	2.38	1.72
3 hours vs. 23	4.37	6.16
16 hours vs. 23	1.69	3.25

* See footnote for Table 4.

ber of non-reinforced responses. Corroboration of this conclusion has been given by Skinner (9), who has demonstrated that animals will make bar-pressing responses when there is zero food deprivation (complete satiation),

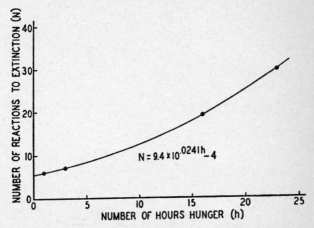

Fig. 5. *Curve showing the number of extinction responses (N) as a function of hunger (h) when the number of previous reinforcements is constant at R = 16. The circles represent the empirical median values from Group B. The curve was plotted by substituting different values for h in the equation shown beneath the graph.*

and by Finch (3), who has demonstrated that conditioned salivary responses occur in satiated dogs.

The curve in Fig. 5 would lead one to expect that as hunger increases indefinitely the behavior potentiality will also increase. Obviously this cannot be the case, since eventually the effects of starvation will begin to act adversely on the behavior potentiality and as the animal nears death from starvation it will be able to make progressively fewer bar-pressing responses. Skinner (9) has obtained a curve of habit potentiality extending out to about six days of food deprivation. His graph shows that behavior potentiality rises with a slight negative acceleration to a maximum at approximately five days, and thereafter declines sharply, many of the animals dying by the sixth day of starvation. Finch (3) has suggested that the curve for the conditioned salivary response in dogs follows a simple parabolic function, rising with a slight negative acceleration to a maximum at about 72 hours of food deprivation and thereafter declining. The above considerations obviously place marked limitations on the generality of equation (4) with its indications of a positively accelerated rise from zero to 23 hours' hunger. Unfortunately, no points between zero and 24 hours are available either in Finch's study or in the related one of Skinner (9). However, the fact that the number of responses at 24 hours' deprivation represents a distinct 'hump' in Skinner's curve between zero and 48 hours' deprivation suggests the possibility of a positively accelerated curve existing between zero and 24 hours in that study.

But why should there be a positive acceleration of behavior potentiality in this particular region of food deprivation which, upon the whole, seems to be negatively accelerated during the first few days? The following tentative hypothesis is offered: in both the Skinner study and the present one, the original reinforcement was carried out at close to 24 hours of hunger. Presumably the hunger stimulations characteristic of this amount of food deprivation make up an important portion of the stimulus complex conditioned to the bar-pressing reaction. Now it has been shown by Hovland (8) that *intensity* of tonal stimulation is generalized.[6] Moreover, it has been shown (7) that *qualitative* generalization follows a marked negatively accelerated falling gradient from the point on the stimulus continuum at which conditioning occurred. It therefore is plausible to assume that there would be a negatively accelerated falling gradient of behavior potentiality from the degree of hunger actually conditioned to any other degree of hunger at which extinction may occur, if no other behavior tendencies were

[6] Hovland (8) has presented evidence for the generalization of intensity of the conditioned stimulus in an experiment using the conditioned galvanic response. He found that the strength of the conditioned response varies inversely with the remoteness of the stimulus from the point which was originally conditioned.

present. On these assumptions it is reasonable to suppose that there would be a typical generalization gradient of behavior potential extending in each direction from 24 hours' food deprivation. This double-winged gradient superposed upon a mildly negatively accelerated curve suggested by the early portions of Skinner's graph (9) would produce the 'hump' in Skinner's curve at 24 hours, and the positive acceleration of Fig. 5 which extends from 0 to 23 hours. This is to say, in effect, that while equation (4) probably represents accurately the experimental results from 0 to about 24 hours under the conditions of both Skinner's experiment and our own, both results are presumably somewhat distorted by generalization effects.

BEHAVIOR POTENTIALITY AS A JOINT FUNCTION OF HABIT STRENGTH AND MOTIVATION

In the statement of results so far, the two groups (A and B), together with Williams' data, have been considered separately. Of far greater importance from the point of view of the present investigation is the manner in which the design of the experiment permits these discrete bits of data to be colligated and treated as a multivariable investigation.

Figure 6 is an orthographic projection with the two independent variables of the investigation occupying the two dimensions of the base and a measure of behavior potentiality (the dependent variable) represented by columns rising perpendicularly in the third dimension. The shaded columns represent the empirical values for the Williams experiment. Moreover, in Fig. 6 the justification for combining the Williams experiment with the results of the present investigation begins to appear. Not only does the curve at 22 hours' hunger parallel the exponential curve for extinction responses at 3 hours' hunger without any significant inversions, but also the results of Group B serve as an important indication of the consistency of this relationship. When the value $h = 22$ is substituted in the equation fitted to Group B (equation 4) the resulting N value falls almost exactly in line with the curve previously fitted to Williams' results. This interpolated N value from equation (4) is represented by

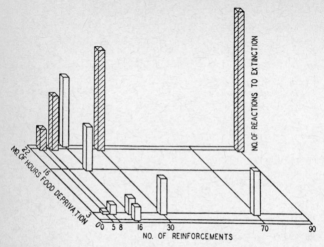

Fig. 6. Three-dimensional representation of the empirical values, the median number of reactions to extinction. The shaded columns are Williams' results; the columns from left to right along the line for 3 hours' food deprivation represent Group A; and the columns running diagonally along the line of 16 reinforcements in the direction of increased deprivation are Group B.

a hollow circle in the graph of the Williams data (Fig. 4). Because of this striking consistency in the number of extinction responses yielded by the two experiments, it has been possible to utilize the Williams data in the mathematical analysis with a confidence otherwise unwarranted.

As pointed out previously, the results of Group A and those of the Williams experiment indicate that behavior potentiality is a simple growth function of the number of reinforcements when hunger at the time of extinction is constant. This coupled with the fact that Group B shows the relation of behavior potentiality to food deprivation, makes it possible to fit a geometrical surface that takes into account all three variables—reinforcement, hunger, and the measure of behavior potentiality.

An equation representing the results presented in Fig.

6 as a curved surface has been derived in the following manner. First, the two growth curves along the reinforcement dimension were extrapolated by substituting $R = \infty$ in equations (2) and (3), in order to find the ultimate limits of the curves which might be expected to obtain from a very large number of reinforcements. Then by assuming that these and all other comparable asymptotes between $h = 0$ and $h = 23$ conform to the same general function of the amount of hunger drive as that fitted to Group B at 16 reinforcements (equation 4), the equation for the asymptotes for the exponential curves was found to be,

$$N = 21.45 \times 10^{.0222h} - 4. \qquad (5)$$

This presumptive curve for the asymptotes is shown in Fig. 7. Finally, by substituting this expression of the generalized asymptotes as a function of drive for the asymptotes in equations (2) and (3), which are otherwise practically identical, the mathematical expression for the surface was found to be

$$N = 21.45 \times 10^{.0222h}(1 - 10^{-.018R}) - 4. \qquad (6)$$

By substituting a number of different combinations of h and R in the above equation and solving for N, enough values of N were easily obtained to permit accurate plotting of the smooth surface, as shown in Fig. 8.

Inspection of Fig. 8 indicates that the conclusions which have already been drawn for individual groups (A and B) should hold approximately for intermediate combinations of hunger and reinforcement if those combinations were subjected to test. Here may be observed the characteristic exponential course that behavior potential values take when the number of reinforcements is increased with drive constant. Here also may be observed the course that behavior potential values take for any given number of hours' hunger (between zero and 22) at the time the response is extinguished. Figure 8 also shows plainly the potential remaining when there is zero hunger. This residual potential turns out to be a definitely positive growth function of the number of reinforcements, with small but finite values. When the number of reinforcements becomes zero, however, the number of responses falls to -4, which represents the distance of absolute zero below the reaction threshold.

Since the surface in Fig. 8 purports to be a graphic

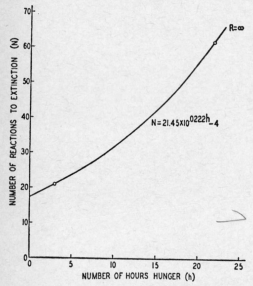

Fig. 7. *Hypothetical curve of the number of extinction responses as a function of hunger when the number of reinforced training trials is infinite. The lower circle represents the probable maximum number of extinction responses for Group A with an infinite number of reinforcements, and the upper circle represents the probable number of extinction responses for Williams' data under the same condition of infinite reinforcement.*

presentation of behavior potentiality as a function of both hunger and reinforcement, the equation for this surface (equation 6) enables us to make a verbal statement of this relationship. Hunger (h) and number of reinforcements (R) appear in exponents within equation (6), with the separate quantities in which h and R appear subsequently being combined as a product. Therefore, the statement can be made that *functions of h and R* combine multiplicatively in their determination of the number of extinction responses as a measure of behavior potentiality. The indication is, further, that the func-

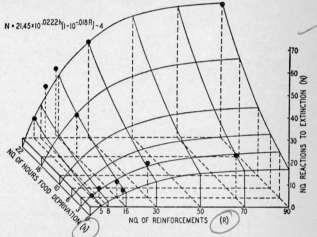

Fig. 8. *Surface fitted to the data in Fig. 6 and Tables 3 and 5. The solid circles represent the empirical values and correspond to the tops of the columns in Fig. 6. The solid curved lines are derived by substituting in the general equation for the surface and are inserted to aid the eye in following the curvature of the surface with changes in food deprivation and reinforcement. The vertical dashed lines are projections from the surface to the plain. The fitted equation describing this surface is in the upper left-hand portion of the figure.*

tion of *h* (whatever it ultimately turns out to be when cleansed from the presumptive contamination of generalization effects) is the asymptote of the expression of which the number of reinforcements is the exponent.

The surface for the time necessary to produce extinction (Fig. 9) has the same general characteristics as the surface for the number of extinction responses, although a more complicated equation was required to yield a reasonably good fit. The equation for the time necessary

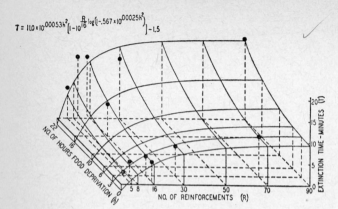

Fig. 9. *The surface for time to extinction as a joint function of hunger and the number of training reinforcements. The equation describing the surface is shown in the drawing.*

for extinction as a joint function of previous reinforcement and hunger when the habit underwent extinction is

$$T = 11.0 \times 10^{.00053h^2}[1 - 10^{\frac{R}{16} \log(1 - .567 \times 10^{.00025h^2})}] - 1.5. \tag{7}$$

The important difference between this equation and the one for number of extinction responses (equation 6) is the fact that food deprivation in equation (7) determines in part the rate of rise of the exponential curves with increased reinforcement. It will be recalled that in the surface for the number of extinction responses, the factor of drive affected only the ultimate limits or asymptotes of the exponential curves, the exponent determining the rates at which these curves approached their asymptotes remaining the same regardless of the drive with which the exponential curve was secured. Certain irregularities in the Williams data on time to produce extinction suggest that equation (6) and Fig. 8 may present a truer picture of the functional relationship here under investigation than do equation (7) and Fig. 9.

This question can be decided only by further experimentation.

Despite the fact that the Williams investigation yielded no data for latency, a surface showing latency as a function of drive and reinforcement has been constructed analogous to Figs. 8 and 9 on the tentative assumption that the general type of curve found for the series of latencies at 3 hours' hunger will also hold for latency at zero and 23 hours' hunger as reinforcements increase. This assumption was arrived at by analogy with the surface for the number of extinction responses in which the exponent determining the rate of change for the reinforcement curve remained unchanged regardless of the amount of food deprivation. When latency is used as a measure of behavior potentiality, a rather different picture results (Fig. 10). This difference arises from the well known fact that latency has an inverse relationship to the other two measures; *i.e.*, the stronger the action potentiality, the shorter the time necessary for a given response to take place when the opportunity presents itself. This relationship may be seen in the drawing of the fitted latency surface (Fig. 10) and in the equation for latency as a function of food deprivation and reinforcement. This is

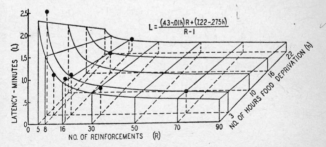

$$L = \frac{(43 - 01h)R + (122 - 275h)}{R - 1}$$

Fig. 10. Surface showing latency as a joint function of hunger and number of training reinforcements. The equation for the surface is shown with the drawing. Comparison with Figs. 8 and 9 shows the inverse relation of latency to the other two measures of behavior potentiality.

$$L = \frac{(.43 - .01h)R + (7.22 - .275h)}{R - 1} \qquad (8)$$

Among other things, the surface and its equation indicate that whenever the number of reinforcements is one or less, the initial latency during extinction will be infinitely great. This is, of course, not surprising, since the surface for extinction responses indicates that no responses will occur when there has been no previous reinforcement (or only one reinforcement); it therefore follows logically that the latency for no response will be infinite. Also, it is to be noted that a substantially linear relation exists between latency and hunger drive as opposed to the positively accelerated curves which were found for extinction time and number of responses as functions of hunger. It must again be emphasized that extrapolation is precarious, especially in the direction of increased hunger, because it would appear from equation (8) that when there are 34.2 hours of hunger with 16 reinforcements having been given previously, the time necessary for an animal to press the bar is zero minutes (latency $= 0$). Obviously a zero latency is a physical impossibility.

SUMMARY

1. The experiment was designed to investigate the joint effect of two antecedent variables on three measures of behavior potentiality. The two antecedent variables were: (I) the number of reinforced repetitions during acquisition of a bar-pressing habit, and (2) the degree of hunger drive as measured by length of food deprivation, when the bar-pressing response underwent extinction. The measures of behavior potentiality were (a) the number of unreinforced responses necessary to produce extinction, (b) the length of time required to extinguish the response, and (c) the latency of the response at the beginning of the extinction period.

2. The subjects were 320 albino rats divided into 8 subgroups of 40 rats each. Four of these subgroups were given 5, 8, 30, and 70 reinforced training trials respectively, and the behavior potentiality was measured when

all the animals had a 3-hour hunger drive. The remaining four subgroups were all given 16 reinforced trials, but had 1, 3, 16, or 23 hours' hunger drive at the time the bar-pressing response was extinguished.

3. The results of an earlier experiment by Williams (10) were found to be quantitatively comparable with the results for the number of extinction responses in the present experiment, and are included in the data from which conclusions are drawn. Williams' results on the time necessary for extinction, while manifesting certain internal inconsistencies as well as deviations from the results of the present experiment, are incorporated in the present investigation though with some reservations.

4. The joint determination of the behavior potentialities by the two antecedent or independent variables can be adequately represented only by means of equations or by curved surfaces. Such equations, accompanied by the curved surfaces corresponding to them, are presented for each of the three measures of behavior potentiality. Of the three, the data for the number of reactions to produce extinction are believed to be the most adequate.

5. A study of these three multiple relationships discloses a striking similarity between the equations and surfaces representing the number of reactions to produce extinction and the time required to produce extinction as joint functions of the antecedent variables (reinforcements and food deprivation). Further experimentation will be necessary to determine whether the differences between equations (6) and (7) are genuine or whether they are due to limitations in the sample. The combination of reinforcements and food deprivation (*habit strength* and *motivation*) to yield values of reaction latency results in a surface and equation of radically different form than those for extinction responses and time.

6. If the equation for the number of reactions required to produce extinction be taken as the true relationship (assuming that the true equation for time to produce extinction would differ only in the value of one or more of the constants) a fairly simple verbal statement of the relationship may be made: behavior potentiality increases as a positive growth (exponential) function of the number of reinforcements, the asymptote of

the growth function being itself a function of the number of hours' food deprivation. The exact functional relationship of this asymptote to motivation in general or even to the number of hours' food deprivation is not clear, though the probability is that it is a slightly negatively accelerated increasing function for deprivation less than 5 or 6 days.

7. However, if the exact mathematical statement be waived, a statement of the relationship may be made with less definiteness but with far greater confidence: (A) The number of extinction reactions and the time required for extinction are both *increasing* functions of the number of previous reinforcements and the number of hours' food deprivation (from zero to about 120 hours). (B) Reaction latency is a *decreasing* function of the same two antecedent variables.

REFERENCES

1. CRUTCHFIELD, R. S., Efficient factorial design and analysis of variance illustrated in psychological experimentation, *J. Psychol.*, 1938, 5, 339-346.

2. ELLSON, D. G., Quantitative studies of the interaction of simple habits. I. Recovery from specific and generalized effects of extinction, *J. exp. Psychol.*, 1938, 23, 339-358.

3. FINCH, G., Hunger as a determinant of conditional and unconditional salivary response magnitude, *Amer. J. Physiol.*, 1938, 123, 379-382.

4. FISHER, R. A., *Design of experiments*, Edinburgh: Oliver and Boyd, 1937.

5. FITTS, P. M., Perseveration of non-rewarded behavior in relation to food-deprivation and work-requirement, *J. genet. Psychol.*, 1940, 57, 165-191.

6. GARRETT, H. E., *Statistics in psychology and education*, New York: Longmans, Green and Co., 1937.

7. HOVLAND, C. I., The generalization of conditioned responses. I. The sensory generalization of conditioned responses with varying frequencies of tone, *J. gen. Psychol.*, 1937, 17, 125-148.

8. ———, The generalization of conditioned responses. II. The sensory generalization of conditioned responses with varying intensities of tone, *J. genet. Psychol.*, 1937, 51, 279-291.

9. SKINNER, B. F., *The behavior of organisms*, New York: D. Appleton-Century Co., 1938.

10. WILLIAMS, S. B., Resistance to extinction as a function of the number of reinforcements, *J. exp. Psychol.*, 1938, 23, 506-522.

11. ———, Transfer of extinction effects in the rat as a function of habit strength, *J. comp. Psychol.*, 1941, 31, 263-280.

14

True, Sham, and Esophageal Feeding as Reinforcements[1]

CLARK L. HULL, JOHNSTON R. LIVINGSTON,
RICHARD O. ROUSE, AND ALLEN N. BARKER
Institute of Human Relations, Yale University

*The following question is posed in this selection: Is
primary drive reduction necessary for the learning of instrumental responses?*

*It is Hull's contention that drive reduction following
the performance of a response is necessary in order for
that response to be learned. The research demonstrates
that an eating response is not sustained when drive reduction does not occur, that is, when food is not permitted to enter the stomach.*

The selection is reprinted from The Journal of Comparative and Physiological Psychology, *1951, 44, 236-245,
with the permission of the authors and the American
Psychological Association.*

Incidental to discussing the status of food reward as
a reinforcing agent, the senior author of this study suggested (5, p. 99) that a sham-feeding experiment on a
specially prepared animal might clarify some of the causal
uncertainties in this field. Recently two somewhat similar
suggestions have also been made (6, 12). The present

[1] The experimental work here reported was performed by
Mr. Livingston, Mr. Rouse, and Mr. Barker, under the super-
vision of the senior author, who planned the investigation and
prepared the manuscript. The three junior authors worked with
the dog, one at a time, until each in turn was called into
military service. The authors are deeply indebted to Dr. G. J.
Connor, of the Yale Medical School, who very kindly performed
the surgical operation producing the two esophageal fistulas on
the dog.

somewhat belated article is the report of an exploratory study in this field.

THE PREPARATION OF THE EXPERIMENTAL ANIMAL AND THE FISTULA LINK

The subject employed in this experiment was a short-haired male mongrel dog weighing 10 kilos when in normal condition. As a means of interrupting at one point the usual relatively uniform chain of stimulating and response events leading from eating to ultimate nutrition, two esophageal fistulas were produced in the animal (Fig. 1). The first stage of the operation brought

Fig. 1. Drawing of the experimental animal illustrating both cut ends of the esophagus externalized to permit the insertion of the esophageal cannula.

a 2-in. segment of the esophagus to the surface of the neck through a slit which was closed by sutures. In three days the esophagus healed to the cut edges of the skin surrounding each end of the segment. Then the exposed segment of esophagus was cut in the middle. The two ends of the previously very taut esophagus segment thereupon retracted to a certain extent, and promptly healed, leaving exposed and protruding the somewhat button-like structures shown in Fig. 1. Both stages of the operation were performed under general anaesthetic.

Because of the taut state of the esophagus during the three

days between the two operations, the dog was unable to swallow anything. During this period he was given two intravenous injections of glucose and water. Following the second operation the animal was fed for a time on a mixture of water and evaporated milk administered by means of a rubber catheter inserted about two inches into the lower fistula. Later this diet was replaced by a thin gruel made of equal parts (100 gm. each) of finely ground Purina Dog Chow and Klim (whole milk powder) stirred up with about 500 cc. of water. This diet is represented by the formula, 100-100-500.

After the operation the dog lost about a kilogram of weight, but most of this was regained within a month. It was also noticed that after the operation the animal showed a marked fear, as indicated by tendencies to flight from the experimenter, trembling, and a general defensiveness. However, after about six weeks of careful feeding and kind treatment involving lavish petting, the dog regained his good spirits, would bark, frisk about, play animatedly with the experimenter, and no longer required restraint when being fed with the catheter.

It is evident from Fig. 1 that when the animal ate his gruel it would flow directly out of the upper fistula, and none of it would go to the stomach. Since this type of feeding fails to yield the animal nutriment, it is called *sham feeding*. In order that *true eating* might take place in an approximately normal manner, a special instrument had to be constructed to link the two fistulas in a functional manner. This link consisted of two pieces of bent glass tubing joined by a section of rather firm rubber tubing inside of which was a piece of tubular metal, as shown in Fig. 2. When under pressure, the two glass ends of this instrument could be brought close enough together to be inserted into the two fistulas. When the insertion had been made and the tube was allowed to resume its natural shape, its increased length tended to hold it in place.[2] Once in position, the ends of the rubber were in direct contact with the respective openings, which aided in avoiding leakage. By means of this tubular esophageal link the animal could eat thin gruel in a fairly normal manner, the gruel passing from one fistula via the tube into the other and thence into the stomach.

At first, when the tubular esophageal link was put in place, the dog would retch a good deal and try to shake the tube out.

[2] However, owing to the shortness of the upper tube section, this portion would sometimes come out of the fistula. Our experience suggests the desirability of placing the upper fistula somewhat lower on the neck, so that this tube section may be longer and thus remain more securely in place without causing retching.

However, the experimenter would hold the dog's mouth closed with the chin well up, as in Fig. 1, and the retching tendency would then gradually subside. The use of the tube in actual eating greatly facilitated elimination of the retching.

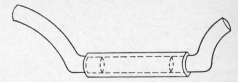

Fig. 2. Drawing of tube connecting the upper and lower esophageal fistulas. The two ends were of glass; the middle opaque section was of rather firm rubber tubing; this contained a third section, of metal tubing (shown in dotted outline). The combination was stiff enough so that it would not buckle under ordinary pressure, but would bend under greater pressure to conform to the dog's head and neck movements. Since the rubber would not enter the fistulas, it served to keep the connecting tube from being drawn into the stomach by peristalsis, and also from being regurgitated by negative peristalsis. The shorter of the two end tubes was the one inserted in the upper fistula. This needed to be short to prevent severe retching.

EXPERIMENT I—CAN "EXPERIMENTAL EXTINCTION" OF EATING BE PRODUCED BY SHAM FEEDING?

METHOD

One of the possibilities we wished to determine was whether eating can be experimentally extinguished by being greatly extended without food going into the stomach, i.e., by sham feeding. In order to investigate this, the dog was given sham feedings to satiation on eight successive evenings at eight o'clock. Each morning at eight the dog was esophagus-fed a 100-100-600 ration of gruel, and in the afternoon at three he was given 500 cc. of water, to be drunk through the esophageal link (Fig. 2). A gruel mixture of 280-280-1700 was placed before the animal in a bowl for sham eating.

In this experiment we needed to know exactly how much gruel was eaten. We accordingly constructed a special device to catch the gruel as it flowed from the upper fistula, and transmit it through a tube to 100-cc. cups located behind a screen. This gruel-catching device was a sort of funnel with the top cut away above and below so as to fit closely the neck of the animal. Its edges were padded with rubber to avoid irritating the animal's skin, and it was strapped firmly to the dog's neck, well above the lower fistula.

Two 100-cc. cups were used in alternation to receive and measure the gruel as it flowed from the catching device. The number of cups thus filled by the sham-eaten gruel was recorded. As the successive cups became full, the gruel was returned to the eating dish by means of the supported vessel and tube (shown at the left in Fig. 4). Saliva was, of course, mixed with the re-eaten food, and the mixture was consequently a little thicker than when first prepared, but trial showed that this did not make the food any less attractive to the animal. Indeed, when in his living quarters, he would avidly lick up the saliva which constantly exuded from the upper fistula.

RESULTS

The quantitative results of this experiment are represented in Fig. 3. This shows that the dog did, in fact, cease his tendency to eat. There it may be seen that the "extinction," or whatever it was in fact, was complete on the eighth day.

Certain accessory observations throw some light on this outcome of the experiment: *Before* the sham feeding on the eighth day the animal was offered, in his living quarters, the choice of gruel versus water twice, and chose food in both cases. He was then taken to the experimental room and placed in the usual sham-feeding situation, but took only two or three licks of the food even when coaxed. Tests given in other parts of the room yielded similar negative results. However, when a parallel test was made a few minutes later in the cage room, the animal promptly ate 150 cc. of the same gruel. These observations indicate that the failure to eat in the experimental room was not due to lack of hunger or incidental motivation.

This experiment needs much to be carefully repeated with a variety of controls. One variation should be to perform the experiment with only normal amounts of food to be sham-eaten, so that extreme eating fatigue would not develop. This practice should continue for a month or two, *with no true eating or drinking whatever*, or at least until true extinction clearly would or would not develop. One test of extinction genuineness would be the presence of spontaneous recovery in the early stages of extinction in case it really develops. The rate of eating should be a valuable index in this test, and otherwise as well.

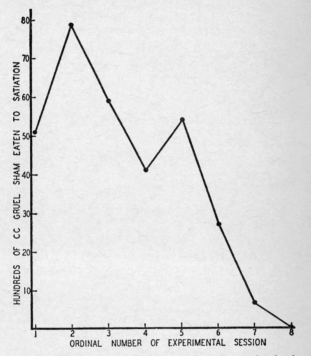

Fig. 3. Graph showing the amount of gruel eaten by the dog in each of the eight sessions during which he was sham fed until he ceased eating for 5 minutes. The low value in the first session was probably due to the attempt to replace sham-fed food in the eating dish, with a cup. This seemed to distract the dog and interrupt eating so that in subsequent sessions the food was slowly and unobtrusively replaced by means of a rubber tube (see Fig. 4). Note that in the second session, before stopping, the dog ate an amount of gruel approaching his body weight.

EXPERIMENT II—CAN A STABLE POSITION HABIT BE SET
UP ON THE BASIS OF REAL FEEDING AS OPPOSED TO SHAM
FEEDING?

The results of Experiment I strongly suggested that
real feeding, even though via the tube shown in Fig. 2,
would be more reinforcing than sham feeding. This pre-
sumption was strengthened by the observation during an
abortive attempt to set up a black-white discrimination
(Fig. 4) on the basis of real versus sham feeding, that if

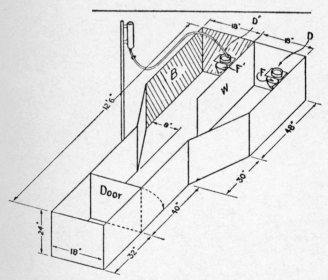

Fig. 4. Simple two-choice maze used with the fistula dog.
This was constructed of quarter-inch wallboard. The section in
the extreme foreground of the figure as far as the door constituted the starting box. The door, hinged at the bottom, lay
flat on the floor when open. D, D', food dishes; F, F', funnels
which caught the gruel flowing from the upper fistula during
the sham feeding of Experiments II and III. The tube leading
to D' from the vessel on the standard at the left was used to
replenish the food dishes without disturbing the dog while
sham feeding. B, black; W, white; the inner walls of the two
food chambers were interchangeable so that in a few seconds
left-black, right-white could be changed to left-white and right-
black.

real feeding was performed consistently on a given side of the maze for a few times the dog would soon come regularly to choose that side. However, in order to secure unambiguous evidence on the point, a special experiment was set up.

METHOD

At the beginning the dog had a strong and uniform tendency to choose the left-hand alley of the maze. Accordingly, in the present experiment when he went into the left-hand alley he was sham-fed until he ceased to eat, but if he went into the right-hand alley, the fistula-linking tube was put in place, and he was allowed to really eat 50 cc. of gruel. Always when a choice was being made, a dish of the gruel was standing conspicuously in each alley. At first, of course, the dog consistently chose the left-hand alley and was there sham-fed (the food continuously being replaced) until he showed marked signs of extinction. Then he was gently led into the right-hand alley and there fed 50 cc. with the tube, after which he was taken back to the starting box (Fig. 4) and given another run.

RESULTS

The progress of the learning in terms of per cent choices of L (sham feeding) or R (real esophageal-link feeding) is shown graphically in Fig. 5. The number of trials per experimental session varied considerably, in general increasing as the experiment progressed; on the first day only three trials were given and on the last, nine. Nevertheless, the outcome, as shown by Fig. 5, is quite definite. Real feeding is clearly much more strongly reinforcing than is sham feeding to near "extinction."

EXPERIMENT III—CAN A STABLE POSITION HABIT BE SET UP ON THE BASIS OF SHAM FEEDING VERSUS NO FEEDING WHATEVER?

METHOD

In order to determine more precisely the relative power of sham feeding in the reinforcement hierarchy, we carried out an experiment in which sham-feeding was put into competition with no food at all. No feeding tube of any sort was necessary for this experiment. At the beginning the dog had a strong left-turning habit. Each alley had its usual dish, but only the one in the right alley contained gruel.

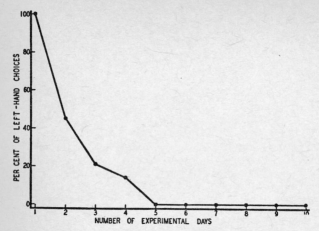

Fig. 5. Graph showing the course of the development of a preference for the right-hand alley as the result of mouth-tube feeding versus sham feeding.

RESULTS

The outcome of this experiment is shown in Table 1. There it may be seen that the dog very promptly changed positions in favor of the sham feeding, and after single relapses, one on each of two subsequent days, continued to make this choice for 18 trials without a failure. Sham feeding, while it has limitations, appears to have definite secondary reinforcing power (2, 3).

TABLE 1

TABLE SHOWING THE ORIGINAL LEFT-HAND CHOICES FOLLOWED BY NON-FEEDING (−) AND THE RIGHT-HAND CHOICES FOLLOWED BY SHAM FEEDING (+)

Note the consistent right-hand choices after the first two or three days.

DATE (1943)	TRIAL NUMBER PER SESSION AND ITS SCORE										
	1	2	3	4	5	6	7	8	9	10	11
February											
23	−	−	−	−	+	−	+	+	+	+	+
24	+	−	+	+	+	+	+	+			
25	−	+	+	+	+	+	+				
26	+	+	+	+	+	+					
March											
1	+	+	+	+	+	+					
2	+	+	+	+	+	+					

This experiment should be repeated with food in *both* dishes, that in the left alley being covered with a coarse screen.

EXPERIMENT IV—CAN A STABLE POSITION HABIT BE SET UP ON THE BASIS OF ESOPHAGEAL FEEDING VERSUS PSEUDO-ESOPHAGEAL FEEDING?

METHOD

In order to explore the principle of reinforcement still further, Experiment IV was set up to determine whether a position preference could be established on the basis of esophageal feeding. The dog was first given a strong left-hand preference on the basis of real feeding. Then he was given a few trials per day in which he ran freely from the starting box to the alley of his choice (Fig. 4). In case the right-hand alley was chosen, the catheter was inserted two inches into the lower fistula and 150 cc. of gruel was permitted to flow into the dog's stomach. This is called *fistula feeding*. In case the dog chose the left-hand alley, as he invariably did at the beginning, the catheter was inserted 2 in. into the lower fistula and left there for 45 sec. (about the usual period required for the esophageal feeding), but no gruel was given. This is called *pseudo-esophageal feeding*.

RESULTS

Unfortunately, the data from this experiment have been lost. However, we have the following memorandum: "An inspection of the table shows that the dog quite promptly learned to choose the alley in which he received food through his esophagus rather than a mere insertion of the catheter." Apparently the outcome of the experiment was clear enough at the time, but it is now in some doubt due to the imperfection of the record.

This experiment needs badly to be repeated with careful controls, especially in respect to the pseudo-esophageal feeding, which should be just as perfect a duplication of the fistula feeding as possible.

DISCUSSION

The present experiment was set up on the basis of the following considerations: Eating is a relatively uniform but complex sequence of gustatory, olfactory, proprioceptive, and other stimulation with the accompanying prehension, mastication, deglutition, digestion, and absorption of the food. If there is a primary reinforcing event at the posterior end of such a uniform sequence, all the events anterior in the series could continue to function indefinitely as secondary reinforcements, maintenance being effected by the gradient of reinforcement (8, 9). It is conjectured, however, that once the primary reinforcing agent is completely removed, the secondary reinforcing agents, if given maximum exercise, will suffer experimental extinction. The sham-feeding experiment was an attempt to discover whether eating and swallowing are such secondary reinforcing processes.

An incidental observation recorded by Bellows and Van Wagenen suggested at the outset that this deduction might be verified. One of their dogs (which were always esophageally fed) ceased altogether to try to eat (1, p. 432). "The temporal muscles became quite atrophic." It may be significant in this connection that the food surreptitiously seized by the dogs usually clogged "in the superior stenosed opening and caused retching." This clogging in the upper fistula presumably constituted fairly effective punishment in addition to a failure of normal nutritional reinforcement. This still further complicates the interpretation by suggesting the operation of negative reinforcement (punishment) as distinguished from experimental extinction.

A possibly related observation made during extended sham feedings is that our dog frequently showed "violent nervous shaking," [3] presumably from the fatigue of eating, which evidently was considerable. It seems likely that this, possibly coupled with the enormous incidental secretion of saliva, may have been an important negatively reinforcing (punishment) factor in causing the cessation from sham eating which we have tentatively labeled "experimental extinction." On the other hand, the Mowrer-Miller hypothesis (5, p. 278) holds that I_R is based on a concept closely related to fatigue, which is akin to punishment.

[3] Quoted from the laboratory notes.

In addition, there is the question of the relative roles played by the hypothetical distinct roles in experimental extinction of (1) work (5, p. 279), and (2) what has been called *frustration* (4, p. 499; 10, p. 482 ff.). This latter principle stated in modern terminology would be the failure of an expectation from being realized. Expectation or "expectancy" would be defined as a fractional anticipatory goal reaction (r_G) based on a stimulus trace (7; 11; 4, p. 495). The connection between the stimulus trace and the response would be brought about by the principle of the delay in reinforcement (8, 9). And the antedating of the realization or goal by the expectation (r_G) would be brought about by generalization (5, p. 183) on the stimulus trace continuum. Presumably, the matter of spontaneous recovery, or its failure to occur, will play a significant role in the latter problem.

Our esophageal feeding involved esophageal peristalsis with its proprioception, which could be avoided by having a stomach fistula (12). This would add another valuable dimension to the experiment, i.e., esophageal fistula feeding versus stomach fistula feeding.

SUMMARY

Through an operation, two esophageal fistulas were produced on a small dog. A semi-flexible, tubular link was made which could be inserted into the fistulas, largely taking the place of the interrupted section of the esophagus. With this link in place, the dog could eat gruel in a fairly normal manner, but without the link, eating was completely sham. Four experiments were performed on this dog. These experiments showed that:

1. In sham feeding, the dog early in the experiment ate about 8 kilos of food before stopping for 5 min., whereas he weighed only 10 kilos before the operation. This cessation of the sham eating occurred on the whole after less eating on each successive test of this sort. These facts suggest experimental extinction from work if not accompanied by adequate reinforcement. Another fact suggesting experimental extinction of the eating activity and conditioned inhibition is that the animal, at the end of the experiment, refused to be sham-fed in the experi-

mental room, but ate readily in his living quarters. This form of behavior soon disappeared, however, with ordinary eating.

2. A stable position choice in a simple maze showed that real eating had much more reinforcing power than sham feeding, which harmonizes with 1.

3. Also, a stable position choice in the maze showed that sham feeding had a much greater (presumably secondary) reinforcing power than did no feeding at all.

4. Finally, esophageal feeding was probably shown to be more strongly reinforcing than pseudo-esophageal feeding in the same maze.

This study is a preliminary exploration and should be repeated and greatly extended with additional controls. Valuable suggestions for related experiments will be found in two recent proposals (6, 12). As a matter of fact, the specific experiment originally proposed (5, p. 99) has not yet been performed. The senior author has no intention of returning to this experiment.

REFERENCES

1. Bellows, R. T., and Van Wagenen, W. P. The relationship of polydipsia and polyuria in diabetes insipidus. *J. nerv. ment. Dis.*, 1938, 88, 417-473.

2. Bugelski, R. Extinction with and without sub-goal reinforcement. *J. comp. Psychol.*, 1938, 26, 121-133.

3. Grice, G. R. The relation of a secondary reinforcement to delayed reward in visual discrimination learning. *J. exp. Psychol.*, 1948, 38, 1-16.

4. Hull, C. L. Goal attraction and directing ideas conceived as habit phenomena. *Psychol. Rev.*, 1931, 38, 487-506.

5. Hull, C. L. *Principles of behavior.* New York: D. Appleton-Century, 1943.

6. Mowrer, O. H. On the dual nature of learning—a re-interpretation of "conditioning" and "problem-solving." *Harv. educ. Rev.*, 1947, 17, 102-148.

7. Pavlov, I. P. *Conditioned reflexes.* (Trans. by G. V. Anrep.) London: Oxford Univ. Press, 1927.

8. Perin, C. T. A quantitative investigation of the delay-of-reinforcement gradient. *J. exp. Psychol.*, 1943, 32, 37-51.

9. Perkins, C. C. The relation of secondary reward to gradi-

ents of reinforcement. *J. exp. Psychol.*, 1947, 37, 377-392.

10. ROHRER, J. H. A motivational state resulting from non-reward. *J. comp. physiol. Psychol.*, 1949, 42, 476-485.

11. SPENCE, K. W. The role of secondary reinforcement in delayed reward learning. *Psychol. Rev.*, 1947, 54, 1-8.

12. TOLMAN, E. C. There is more than one kind of learning. *Psychol. Rev.*, 1949, 56, 144-155.

15

Reward Value of a Non-Nutritive Sweet Taste

FRED D. SHEFFIELD AND THORNTON B. ROBY
Institute of Human Relations, Yale University

The following paper represents a criticism of the universality of the principle of drive reduction in learning. The point that Sheffield and Roby make is that the absence of a drive-reducing stimulus following performance of the response does not seem to prevent learning. Rather, they show that any stimulus which produces a consummatory response will reinforce the conditioned response.

Saccharine, a non-nutritive chemical and therefore a non-drive reducing substance, is capable of reinforcing new learning, and this learning is as persistent as that which is reinforced with nutritive food. The authors interpret these results as indicating that any stimulus which produces an eating response will reinforce new learning and that drive reduction is not a necessary characteristic of reinforcing stimuli.

This selection is reprinted from The Journal of Comparative and Physiological Psychology, 1950, 43, 471-481, *with the permission of the authors and the American Psychological Association.*

The purpose of the present experiments was to help answer the question of what constitutes a "reinforcing state of affairs" in instrumental conditioning. One of the most systematic positions on this topic (4) holds that ultimate reduction of a survival need is an essential factor, and a closely related position (5) argues for the necessity of ultimate reduction in a primary drive. However, several studies (3, 6, 1)—and at least one theory of reinforcement (10)—suggest the possibility that a sweet taste is reinforcing regardless of whether it is produced by a nutritive or non-nutritive substance. These previous studies demonstrate that sweet-flavored water is preferred to plain water by rats. They do not demonstrate, however, whether a sweet taste, per se, will operate as a reward in instrumental conditioning, uncomplicated either by a measurement of purely reflexive ingestion or by acquired reward from nutritive sweet-tasting substances. Also previous studies apparently have not related the sweet preference to the hunger state of the animal. The present experiments demonstrate that a non-nutritive sweet-tasting substance functions as a very effective reward in instrumental conditioning. They also demonstrate that the reward value depends on the degree of hunger present.

The "reward" used for instrumental conditioning in rats was a solution of saccharine in water. This substance produces a sweet taste in humans which is apparently "satisfying" to its many users (chiefly diabetics and those on reducing diets). The non-nutritive nature of saccharine is indicated by the fact that it apparently goes through the mammalian body unchanged chemically, and animals ingesting it do not diminish their food intake (3). Throughout all the present experiments the solution used was 1.30 grams of pure saccharine powder per liter of water. This value was chosen on the basis of a previous investigation of sweet preference (1) as likely to be effective with most rats.

EXPERIMENT I

PURPOSE

The purpose of Experiment I was to determine whether a position preference in drinking behavior could be established on the basis of saccharine flavored water and whether the preference varied as a function of degree of hunger.

METHOD

Six albino rats (age about six months at outset of experiment) were kept hungry by restricting their daily diet to eight grams (dry weight) of ground Purina Dog Chow mixed with 10 cc. of water. Six comparable control animals had food available at all times in the form of standard dry Purina Dog

Chow pellets. The living cages were equipped at their rear walls with two 100 cc. graduated cylinders about four inches apart which served as water bottles. The cylinders were held in place by standard steel-clip broom holders, which permitted rapid insertion or removal without dripping of the contents. The water was taken by the rat in the usual way—by lapping from the end of a glass tube. The tips were partially sealed to a diameter small enough to prevent any spontaneous dripping. The laboratory was dimly lighted by a shielded 25-watt lamp at all times except when readings were made and when the daily food was given, at which times a bright overhead light was turned on. The procedure was as follows:

1. Two habituation days in the cages with both groups satiated for food and water, followed by a day in which the six experimental animals were not fed.

2. Five days with water in both bottles, hunger-drive regime as indicated in the Method section.

3. Nineteen days of alternate training and testing. On *training* days a saccharine solution (1.30 grams per liter) was on a given side for a given animal, water being on the other side; on the alternate *testing* days water was on both sides. The saccharine side was on the left for half of the animals of each group and on the right for the other half.

RESULTS

Relative consumption of water and saccharine solution: All animals demonstrated rapid acquisition of a preference for drinking the saccharine solution as compared with the water solution on training days. Regardless of the degree of hunger, the proportion—of total liquid consumed—taken from the saccharine bottle jumped to almost 100 per cent during the first training day. The relevant results are shown in Table 1.

Table 1 shows that there was a slight preference in both groups for the "saccharine" side prior to the introduction of saccharine, as indicated by the per cent of water intake during the preceding day when there was water in both bottles. During the first 2½ hours with saccharine in one of the bottles, however, there was a decided preference in both groups for drinking from the saccharine bottle, and over the entire first 24 hours with saccharine both groups drank almost exclusively from the saccharine bottle. There was little difference between the first and last day of training.

TABLE 1

Acquisition of Drinking from the Saccharine Side on Training Days

| | MEAN PER CENT FROM SACCHARINE SIDE OUT OF TOTAL INTAKE OF FLUID FROM BOTTLES | | | |
	Preceding day (water in both bottles)	During first 2½ training hours	During first training day	During tenth training day
Hungry...	55.2	88.6	98.8	99.5
Satiated...	59.5	77.3	95.5	95.8

Whereas there was no important difference between hungry and satiated animals in the *per cent* of total intake from the saccharine bottle, there was a large difference in *absolute* intake. Hungry animals drank far more saccharine solution than satiated animals. This is shown in Table 2, which also compares saccharine drinking with water consumption prior to the first training day.

It can be seen in Table 2 that both hungry and satiated rats markedly increased their fluid intake when the saccharine solution was available. Even satiated animals almost doubled their intake, while the hungry animals increased theirs by a factor of almost nine, drinking over two and one-half times as much of the solution as the

TABLE 2

Effect of Hunger on Consumption of Saccharine Solution

| | MEAN CCS. FLUID TAKEN | | | | |
	From both water bottles before training	From saccharine bottle during training	Diff.	*t*	df.
Hungry.	24.2	205.4	181.2	9.7	5
Satiated	37.8	78.1	40.3	4.8	5
Diff.....	−13.6	127.3			
t........	3.7	6.0			
df......	10	10			

satiated animals. It will also be noted that hungry animals drank significantly less water than satiated animals during the five control days before the introduction of saccharine. This may well merely reflect the fact that they received 10 cc. of water in their daily ration of Purina mash. If a constant of 10 cc. is added to the mean it becomes 34.2 and does not differ significantly from that of the satiated group. Thus no clear relation of hunger to water intake is in evidence.

Position preference on test days: All animals showed a preference for the "saccharine" side during the nine interspersed test days on which there was plain water in both bottles. However, the transfer of position preference was not complete, that is, while all animals drank the *majority* of their water from the reinforced side they did not attain the 100 per cent level. On the contrary, the transfer to test days reached a maximum on the second test day and declined thereafter. The important trends are shown in Table 3.

TABLE 3

MEAN PER CENT OF WATER TAKEN FROM THE "SACCHARINE" SIDE ON TEST DAYS DURING TRAINING

| | MEAN PER CENT FROM "SACCHARINE" SIDE | | | | |
	DAY BEFORE TRAINING	1st TEST DAY	2nd TEST DAY	3rd TEST DAY	9th TEST DAY
HUNGRY	55.2	81.1	82.8	76.7	72.8
SATIATED	59.5	76.7	80.2	68.0	57.3

It can be seen in Table 3 that transfer of the reinforced position to test days with water only increased to the second test day. At this point both hungry and satiated animals showed reliable transfer (*p* less than .02 in each group). But the transfer began to decline by the third test day and continued downward through the remainder of training. The decline from the second to the last test day was not significant for either group but at least the failure to progress toward 100 per cent preference indicates either that the reinforcing power of the saccharine solution was extinguishing or that some other factor was interfering with complete transfer of the position preference to the test days with water in both bottles. One such interfering factor might be frustration due to failing to find a sweet taste in the appropriate bottle on test days. Another could be acquisition of a discrimination involving drinking exclusively from the saccharine side on training days and drinking more or less indiscriminately on the test days. The cue for the differential behavior would be presence or absence of a sweet taste. The critical question for the present study was whether or not the sweet taste was losing its reinforcing power as would be the case if it were an acquired reward. Evidence on this question will be considered next.

Did the reinforcing effect extinguish?: Perhaps the most relevant finding on this question has already been shown in Table 1, in which it is obvious that an almost 100 per cent preference for the saccharine side was maintained throughout the training days for all animals. If the decline in preference on test days is due to decline of reinforcing effect, a comparable decline would be expected on training days.

Another relevant source of evidence is the course of saccharine drinking throughout the 10 training days. The finding here was an initial drop in saccharine drinking in both groups, but with little change from the second to the tenth training day. These results are shown in Table 4. The table shows a significant drop between the first and second training days in the hungry group. None of the other differences shown is significant although the difference in each case is in the direction of extinction of saccharine drinking.

While the results demonstrate some initial extinction of saccharine drinking, they do not provide a convincing explanation of the failure to achieve 100 per cent transfer of position preference on test days. This preference declined *after* the saccharine drinking stabilized. Moreover, a decline in saccharine drinking is not necessarily an index of a decline in its reinforcing power—it could be acquisition of a tendency not to get too full a stomach. It should be noted that ingestion of 245 ccs. of fluid (the mean for the first day for hungry rats) involves consider-

TABLE 4

POSSIBLE EXTINCTION OF SACCHARINE DRINKING

| | | DAY OF SACCHARINE TRAINING | | |
		1st	2nd	10th
Hungry	Mean ccs.	244.7	195.5	194.8
	Diff.		49.2	0.7
	t		4.3	0.1
	df.		5	5
Satiated	Mean ccs.	94.7	77.3	74.3
	Diff.		17.4	3.0
	t		1.6	0.4
	df.		5	5

able stomach distension in a 350-gram animal. The amount consumed is comparable to a 150-pound man's consuming 13 gallons of fluid in a 24-hour period.[1]

EXPERIMENT II

PURPOSE

It had originally been expected that if a sweet taste was reinforcing a progressive acquisition of a position preference on test days would have been shown in Experiment I. This expectation was not borne out; instead the animals showed rapid acquisition of a moderate preference, followed by a tendency toward a decline.

The results might be interpreted as evidence that the reinforcing effect of a sweet taste was relatively weak and tended to extinguish in the course of the experiment. On the other hand the results can be interpreted as evidence that the animal was frustrated by absence of a sweet taste on test days or that a discrimination was being established such that the animals

---

[1] The experimenters had no real check on how much of the saccharine solution was actually ingested because the cages had wire mesh floors with sawdust trays underneath. However, in Experiment III, in which drinking was done over solid floors, very little of the saccharine solution taken was found to be spilled on the floor. In any case the measure used was a good index of instrumental tongue movements.

would try both bottles and drink only from the sweet side if one was sweet, but drink more indiscriminately if neither was sweet. Experiment II was designed to test further the reinforcing value of a sweet taste with both of these latter factors—frustration and discrimination—eliminated.

METHOD

The laboratory was normally kept dimly lighted by a shielded 25-watt lamp. At 9:00 A.M., 11:00 A.M., 1:00 P.M., 3:00 P.M., and 5:00 P.M., the experimenter entered the room, turned on a bright overhead light and inserted the saccharine bottle, always on the same side for a given animal. A bottle of plain water was always present on the opposite side. The subjects were the same ones which had been used in Experiment I, the hunger regime was the same, and the saccharine solution was of the same concentration (1.30 grams per liter) and on the same side as in Experiment I. On each trial the saccharine bottle was left in position for exactly 10 minutes and the measure of instrumental behavior was the amount of the solution consumed. It was expected that if a sweet taste was reinforcing then the turning on of the light, the presence of the experimenter, the sound of the bottle being inserted, and the visual presence of the bottle would be a cue-pattern to which approach and drinking would become conditioned. The ten-minute trials were continued for 18 days—a total of 90 trials.

RESULTS

Acquisition of instrumental drinking in response to the environmental cue-pattern appeared to continue throughout the 18-day period for hungry animals, although approaching an asymptote toward the end of training. Satiated animals on the other hand showed no signs of acquisition. The results are depicted in Fig. 1, which shows the average ccs. per 10-minute trial per rat. The results are smoothed in the figure by using successive sets of three days' trials (15 trials per rat for each point on the curve).

It is apparent in Fig. 1 that the satiated rats show no increase in propensity to drink saccharine whereas hungry animals show progressive acquisition. The acquisition in hungry animals is well beyond the one per cent level of confidence (t, for first point versus last point, $= 4.9$, df. $= 5$). Thus when the frustration and discrimination possible in Experiment I are eliminated a conventional

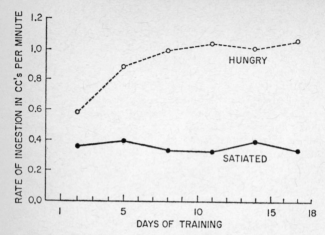

Fig. 1. Acquisition of drinking of the saccharine solution (1.30 grams per liter) in response to a specific cue-pattern accompanying availability of the solution.

acquisition curve is obtained. This argues against extinction of an acquired reward as an explanation of the failure to get progressive acquisition in Experiment I.

It should be borne in mind that the same animals were used in both experiments. Thus a sweet taste was shown to retain its reinforcing value for hungry animals over a lengthy period in which it could have extinguished if it were an acquired reward. Also the rate of ingestion for hungry animals was much higher by the end of Experiment II than it was even on the first day of Experiment I. Over the first day of Experiment I the hungry animals drank at a rate of 0.17 ccs. per minute, whereas the last point on the curve for hungry animals in figure 1 represents a rate of 1.09 ccs. per minute.[2] This difference

[2] A methodological point worth mentioning is that the hungry animals consistently drank the least at the 1:00 P.M. test, which came just before their daily feeding—at a time when they were presumably most hungry. This runs counter to the overall relation between hunger and saccharine drinking and is interpreted by the writers as due to the conflicting habit of loitering at the front of the cage where food was soon to be introduced.

is complicated by the fact that in Experiment I the animals were asleep part of the time but it probably reflects in addition the fact that the unlimited drinking periods of Experiment I allowed any painful effects of too full a stomach to motivate avoidance of drinking behavior. The difference is in a direction opposed to the hypothesis that a sweet taste is an acquired reward which extinguishes with performance of the instrumental response. The reinforcing effect was still going strong after 10 days of unlimited drinking in Experiment I and 18 days with five 10-minute drinking periods per day in Experiment II.

EXPERIMENT III

PURPOSE

The main purpose of Experiment III was to test the reinforcing value of a sweet taste in a more conventional animal-learning situation than that used in Experiments I and II. A second purpose was to continue the same animals in a further learning task to give further opportunity for the reward value of a sweet taste to extinguish if it is an acquired reward. A third purpose was to get a rough idea of the order of magnitude of the reinforcing values of saccharine and food with hungry animals.

METHOD

The same hungry animals used in Experiments I and II served as subjects in Experiment III. Of the six hungry rats used in the first two experiments, one died of whirling disease between experiments, so only five animals were available for Experiment III. The learning task was acquisition of a position habit in a standard T-maze. The stem and each arm of the maze were 21 inches long and four and one-half inches wide. The interior of the stem was painted grey, that of one arm was painted white and that of the other black. The ends of each goal box were made of wire screening to provide cues very similar to those in the animal's previous experience with drinking from the saccharine bottle in its wire-screen living cage. A Springfield timer recorded running time via a microswitch which started the timer when the door of the starting box was opened and another microswitch which stopped the clock when the animal's weight landed on a hinged floor at the far end of the arm. Retracing was prevented by dropping a door as soon as the animal entered a particular arm. The correct side for a given animal always had a bottle of saccharine solution (1.30 grams per liter); the incorrect side had a bottle of plain water. Throughout Experiment III the animals had a supply of water from a water tray in their living cages—thus they were satiated for thirst, and the only time they drank from a glass tube during the experiment was in the maze. All trials were run in the evening, starting about 8:00 P.M.; the daily feeding of 8 grams (dry weight) of Purina flour mixed with water was given at noon. The procedure was as follows:

1. Four forced runs, two to the saccharine side and two to the water side. The forced runs were spaced over two days, one of each kind per day, balanced for order. On each trial the rat was confined in the end box for eight minutes.

2. Forty-two free-choice trials, three per day for 14 days, the trials on a given day being spaced about one half-hour apart. On each trial the rat was confined in the end box for four minutes.

RESULTS

All animals showed prompt acquisition in terms of both time and errors. The results are summarized in the three curves shown in Fig. 2. Curve A shows acquisition in terms of frequency of correct choice; the frequency scores plotted use per cent of correct choices on each day's set of three trials for the five animals. Thus the N at each point in the curve is 15 animal-trials. Curve B

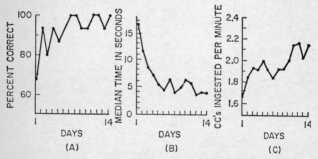

Fig. 2. Acquisition in a T-maze with saccharine solution (1.30 grams per liter) as reward: (A) frequency of correct choices, (B) time to reach correct side, (C) rate of ingestion of solution in the goal box.

shows acquisition in terms of time to reach the end of the arm on correct choices. Every animal made at least one correct choice per day, and the value plotted in the curve is the median, over the five animals, of each animal's median daily performance. Curve C shows the mean rate of consumption of saccharine solution. The daily rate per minute was determined for each animal and these values were averaged over the five animals to get the points plotted.

An important relationship was found between rate of ingestion of saccharine solution and maze performance. Animals whose rate of drinking tended to be low during the four minutes of confinement in the goal box also tended to be poor learners both in terms of time scores and frequency scores. In other words if they did not drink the saccharine avidly they also did not perform well in getting to the solution. The relationship is depicted in Fig. 3.

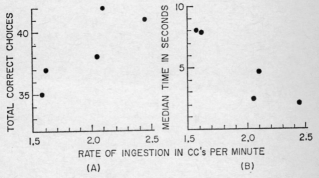

Fig. 3. Relation between mean amount of saccharine drinking in the four-minute confinement and (A) frequency of correct choice on all trials and (B) median running time during the last half of training.

Another interesting finding was that the average rate of consumption was much greater in Experiment III than in either of the preceding experiments. It has already been noted that the rate of ingestion was much greater in Experiment II than in Experiment I and a comparison of figure 1 and figure 2-C readily shows that the ingestion rate was much greater in Experiment III. The last point on the curve in Experiment II showed a rate of 1.09 ccs. per minute whereas the last day in Experiment III was 2.16 ccs. per minute. This result probably can be attributed to the greater specificity of the cues in the maze situation and to the fact that only four minutes of drinking were allowed at a time, thus minimizing the chance of filling up and avoiding the bottle. However, this result, like the rest of the findings in Experiment III, argues against extinction of the reward value of the non-nourishing sweet taste.

Moreover, the motivating power of the sweet taste was quite impressive. The two fastest animals appeared to run at top speed and were consistently close to two seconds at the end of training. The final median time of 3.8 seconds is slower than that obtained in the same apparatus by other rats rewarded with food, who achieved a median of about two seconds. However, the time is still of a low enough order of magnitude to indicate considerable reinforcement value of a sweet taste for hungry animals.

DISCUSSION

The experiments prove that a non-nourishing but sweet-tasting substance served as a reinforcement for instrumental learning. Hunger was presumably in no way reduced by the saccharine solution, yet hungry animals clearly demonstrated acquisition in the three different learning situations in which the reward was a saccharine solution.

The possibility that the sweet taste was an acquired reward seems very unlikely—on two counts. For one thing, previously experienced sweet tastes (e.g., rat's milk, conversion of starch to sugar in the mouth, etc.) are very unlikely to have been as sweet as the concentrated saccharine solution used. Thus the sweet taste used would be at an unfavorable point on the generalization gradient as an acquired reward stimulus if we make the usual assumption that the generalization gradient falls in either direction from the stimulus intensity reinforced. Moreover, the sweet taste did not lose its reward value throughout the three experiments, with the ingestion of thousands of ccs. of saccharine solution and no doubt millions of instrumental tongue movements. Since the visual, kinesthetic, tactile, and gustatory pattern accompanying this ingestion in all three experiments (drinking from a glass tube protruding from a visible graduated cylinder through quarter-inch wire mesh) received no primary reinforcement, it would be expected that any *acquired* reward value of a sweet taste would have extinguished for this pattern.

The findings are thus at variance with the molar principle of reinforcement used by Hull (4), which identifies primary reinforcement with "need reduction." Hull admittedly chose need reduction on the grounds that from a Darwinian point of view reduction of a survival need is very likely to be accompanied by a "reinforcing state of affairs," and at the molar level this principle may be predictive in a high proportion of instances of instrumental learning. However, it does not designate the *mechanism* by which natural selection has managed to make need-reducing events reinforcing, and it is unable to predict the present results in which reinforcement is obtained in the absence of need reduction. The findings highlight the desirability of a theory concerning the mechanism (or mechanisms) by which natural selection has achieved adaptive instrumental learning.

At a more molecular level, Miller and Dollard (5) have proposed *reduction of drive* as the occasion for a reinforcing state of affairs and they tentatively identify drive with intensity of stimulation. The present findings are at variance with their position in that hunger drive, in the usual sense of the concept, is not at all reduced by the saccharine solution. Thus, as mentioned earlier, saccharine is allegedly excreted without chemical change and its ingestion has no effect on food intake (3). However, it may be postulated that part of the total stimulation in the case of hunger consists of proprioceptive return from the striped-muscle tension occasioned by the hunger state. It may further be postulated that a sweet taste relaxes the striped muscles—at the very least the animal stands still while ingesting the solution—and this innate relaxation would provide stimulus reduction and consequent acquisition of instrumental responses. Thus a closer analysis of the physiological effects of a sweet taste may show that the present results are consistent with Miller and Dollard's position.

While the experiments were aimed mainly at providing evidence relevant to the need-reduction and drive-reduction theories, a brief comment should be made on the relation of the results to other positions on the reinforcement process. The results in no way conflict with or provide support for the relatively empirical and circular systems of Skinner (7), Thorndike (8), and Tolman (9). The results merely demonstrate that with hungry animals a saccharine solution is a "reinforcing stimulus" in Skinner's terms, is a "reward" or "satisfier" in Thorndike's terms, and probably is "demanded" in Tolman's terms. The results are also consistent with Guthrie's (2) more theoretical and less circular position involving the mechanism of stimulus change and protection of the last response from relearning. In Guthrie's terms the results demonstrate that ingesting the sweet substance innately produces a stimulus change which can be observed to be very much the same as that produced by presenting food to the hungry animal (i.e., cessation of exploration, maintained ingestion, and so forth) and it is therefore not surprising that the change is big enough to protect the instrumental response. Another theory which cannot escape mention in the present context is the unpopular "beneceptor" theory of Troland (10), which holds that the reinforcing value of a reward lies in the quality of the stimulation produced by the reward. The findings are a natural fit to his theory—which argues that stimulation of receptors for sweet is all that is needed to strengthen an instrumental act.

In conclusion the question should be answered as to whether any novel hypotheses concerning the reinforcement process are indicated by the results. The chief suggestion the authors have to make is that stimulation and performance of a consummatory response appears to be more important to instrumental learning—in a primary, not acquired, way—than the drive satisfaction which the consummatory response normally achieves. The present experiments were essentially sham-feeding experiments in which the animal was innately stimulated to ingest a substance which did not change his state of hunger, and the result was acquisition, without extinction, of the instrumental responses. Thus it would appear that *eliciting* the consummatory response of ingestion was the critical factor. This suggestion is in line with Wolfe and Kaplon's (11) finding that with total food intake held constant, the reward value of eating is a function of amount of consummatory activity required to ingest the food.

SUMMARY

1. A non-nourishing but sweet-tasting substance was shown in three successive learning situations to be an effective reward for instrumental learning, its reward value depending on the state of hunger present.

2. The possibility that the sweet taste was an acquired reward rather than a primary reward was shown to be extremely unlikely.

3. The findings demonstrate the expected limitations of Hull's molar "need reduction" theory of reinforcement and the necessity of exploring indirect reduction of striped-muscle tension as a drive-reduction factor in Miller and Dollard's theory of reinforcement. The results are consistent with Guthrie's last-response theory of reinforcement, and demonstrate that a sweet taste is "reinforcing" in Skinner's system, "satisfying" in Thorndike's system, and "demanded" in Tolman's system.

4. It is suggested that elicitation of the consummatory response appears to be a more critical *primary* reinforcing factor in instrumental learning than the drive reduction subsequently achieved.

REFERENCES

1. Beebe-Center, J. G., Black, P., Hoffman, A. C., and Wade, Marjorie.: Relative per diem consumption as a measure of preference in the rat. *J. comp. physiol. Psychol.* 1948, 41, 239-251.

2. Guthrie, E. R.: *The psychology of learning.* New York: Harper, 1935.
3. Hausmann, M. F.: The behavior of rats in choosing food. II Differentiation between sugar and saccharine. *J. comp. Psychol.* 1933, 15, 419-428.
4. Hull, C. L.: *Principles of behavior.* New York: Appleton-Century, 1943.
5. Miller, N. E. and Dollard, J.: *Social learning and imitation.* New Haven: Yale Press, 1941.
6. Richter, C. P. and Campbell, Kathryne.: Taste thresholds and taste preferences of rats for five common sugars. *J. Nutrition.* 1940, 20, 31-46.
7. Skinner, B. F.: *The behavior of organisms.* New York: Appleton-Century, 1938.
8. Thorndike, E. L.: *Animal intelligence.* New York: Macmillan, 1911.
9. Tolman, E. C.: *Purposive behavior in animals and men.* New York: Appleton-Century, 1932.
10. Troland, L. T.: *The fundamentals of human motivation.* New York: Van Nostrand, 1928.
11. Wolfe, J. B. and Kaplon, M. D.: Effect of amount of reward and consummative activity on learning in chickens. *J. comp. Psychol.* 1941, 31, 353-361.

16

Reward Value of Copulation
Without Sex Drive Reduction[1]

FRED D. SHEFFIELD, J. JEPSON WULFF,
and ROBERT BACKER
Yale University

This article shows that the sexual response of copulation in the absence of ejaculation can reinforce new responses. Ejaculation is considered by Sheffield, et al., as sex drive reduction, and because animals learn to leap a barrier in order to copulate without ejaculating, these results are interpretable in terms of learning in the absence of drive reduction.

This selection is reprinted from The Journal of Comparative and Physiological Psychology, 1951, 44, 3-8, *with the permission of the authors and the American Psychological Association.*

PROBLEM

The purpose of the experiment was to determine whether sexual stimulation in male rats without any associated sex-drive reduction through ejaculation would reinforce the learning of responses instrumental in bringing about the stimulation.

Anecdotal evidence at the human level suggests that erotic stimulation is reinforcing regardless of whether it terminates in orgasm or in a heightened drive state. If so, the learning thus obtained is contrary to the expectation from need reduction or drive reduction theories of reinforcement (5, 7). However, the anecdotal evidence is contaminated with the possibility of social rewards, ac-

---

[1] The authors are greatly indebted to Professor Frank A. Beach of Yale University for guidance in the specialized techniques of rodent sex-behavior study.

quired reward supported by primary drive reduction from auto-erotic stimulation, and so forth. The present experiment using rats as subjects gives more definitive evidence on the reinforcing value of sexual stimulation.

METHOD

Male rats were bred in the Yale laboratories and placed in segregation from females shortly after weaning. When sexually mature (over one hundred days) they were tested for the sex instinct 12 times with females in heat. On the basis of the tests three groups were selected: two of these were matched groups of males which had initiated copulation once or more in the 12 tests, and the third was a group which had shown "interest" but had not copulated in the tests. The two matched groups were then put in an instrumental learning situation in which the reward object in one group (Experimental Group) was a female in heat and in the other (Control Group) a male "companion." The third group (Non-copulators) was subdivided into one half which received a female in heat and another which received a male companion during instrumental learning. Both in tests and in the instrumental learning, rats with female lures were allowed to initiate copulation, but the female was always withdrawn before ejaculation.

Rats were particularly convenient subjects for the experiment because their copulatory pattern (1, 10) makes it relatively easy to control amount of sexual stimulation and to remove the female after a set amount of copulatory activity. Thus the male pattern consists of a series of discrete mountings with rapid pelvic thrusts ending in intromission and vigorous dismounting. This pattern is usually repeated a dozen or more times before the first ejaculation (10). A specified number of such discrete copulatory acts can therefore be allowed as reward for instrumental learning—and the number of these "copulations" can be made too few for ejaculation ever to be at all likely. Moreover the ejaculation pattern is easily recognized—as is the "vaginal plug" left in the female—so that if an animal should happen to ejaculate he could be eliminated from the experiment. Also, since the male dismounts after each copulatory response, the female can be removed without forcible separation.

APPARATUS AND PROCEDURE

The instrumental learning situation consisted of a screen-covered runway ending in a four-inch wire screen hurdle on the far side of which was the entry to the goal box in which the males in the experimental group found a female in heat. The runway was 32 inches long by 8 inches high and wide. It was equipped with a hinged platform at the starting end and another just beyond the hurdle at the entrance to the goal box. The weight of the animal on the start platform started an electric clock which was stopped by the weight of the animal on the platform beyond the hurdle. The instrumental response was getting to the goal box, and its objective measure of strength was the speed as determined from the clocked interval. The goal box had a sawdust-covered floor and was circular, with a 30-inch diameter; it essentially duplicated standard equipment for observing copulation in rats (1). A door at the entrance to the goal box prevented retracing once the latter was entered.

To guarantee receptivity all females used as lures had been spayed and were brought into heat artificially by appropriately spaced injections of estrogen and progesterone.[2] Several females were injected at a time and only those used which demonstrated typical heat behavior (9) with an experienced "indicator" male in a warming-up session just before serving as lures in the experiment. To maintain good heat behavior, good male copulators were alternated with poor ones in training trials. A given female was used only once a week.

Twenty-four hooded males were bred for the experiment and tested for the sex instinct prior to instrumental learning. The 12 preliminary tests were made in the goal box of the apparatus. During these tests only four "copulations" were allowed per test. Of the 24 animals only eight copulated at least once in the 12 tests.[3] These were divided into two groups of four each, matched for copulatory activity during tests, one to receive the female lure (Experimental) and one to receive the male companion (Control) during the experiment proper. Six additional animals who showed sustained pursuit of the female but never copulated were selected to serve as the additional controls (Noncopulators), half to receive male and half to receive female lures during training. One of these died of whirling disease during

[2] The usual injection procedure was 0.25 cc. of Ciba Benovocylin (0.333 mg./cc.) 52 hours before use followed by 0.25 cc. of Ciba Lutocylin (2 mg./cc.) 12 hours before use. The authors wish to express their appreciation to Dr. J. Harold Walton and Dr. Ernst Oppenheimer of Ciba Pharmaceutical Products, Inc., for donating a supply of these expensive hormones for the experiment.
[3] It has subsequently been shown (2) that males are maximally likely to copulate only if they are maintained on a light-dark cycle and tested during the dark part of their cycle. The present animals were kept in a windowless room with no particular light-dark cycle.

the training, so the results of only five non-copulators will be shown.

In training trials the lure was always placed in the goal box immediately after the subject entered the box and was removed after two copulations (or two attempts in the case of male "lures") or after two minutes if two copulations were not achieved in that period. Subjects were removed from the goal box 15 seconds after removal of the lure. If a subject dallied longer than two minutes in the runway, he was placed over the hurdle; if he then dallied for another minute without entering the goal box he was placed directly in the box. Learning trials were run at night in a room lighted only by a 100-watt lamp directly above the goal box. Each subject had two massed trials per training night, and training nights were spaced two days apart. Twenty-eight learning trials were given in all.

RESULTS

The major results are depicted in the learning curves shown in Fig. 1. Speed of running (100/time in seconds) is the dependent variable. It can be seen in the figure that all groups showed some indication of acquisition. However, the experimental copulators who received female lures are superior both to non-copulators and to control copulators who received male lures. The superiority is in each case significant beyond the 5 per cent level of confidence whether all 28 trials are used or whether only the last training trial is used. In the figure the curves have been smoothed by combining appropriate groupings of trials.

An unexpected result seen in Fig. 1 is that copulator controls performed better than non-copulators. The difference is not highly significant ($p = .08$ for one tail, using all 28 trials), but other evidence indicates that a real difference is involved due to *attempted copulation* on the part of copulators who received a male lure. The additional evidence is shown in Fig. 2, in which mean speed over all 28 trials is plotted as a function of number of attempted copulations for all subjects regardless of the sex of the lure. It can be seen that a single regression line seems to be involved in which sex of lure appears to be irrelevant except in determining whether or not the copulatory act (mounting and thrusts) is elicited. Thus

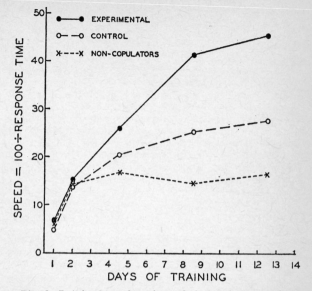

Fig. 1. *Reinforcing value of copulation without ejaculation. Experimental animals found a female in the goal box, control animals found a male, and non-copulators found one or the other but never attempted to copulate.*

the subjects with male lures (open circles) and subjects with female lures (filled circles) are intermingled in the scatter-plot shown in Fig. 2. This indicates that the superior acquisition of the Experimental Group is due, not to the intromission that accompanied copulatory responses with females, but rather to the greater frequency with which copulatory responses were elicited by the females.

The result in Fig. 2 probably reflects acquired drive (or acquired reward) based on the preliminary tests in the goal box. In these tests all copulators learned to approach and mount the receptive female in the goal box. When a male was used as lure with copulator controls during instrumental training, this prior learning apparently transferred and the subjects went through the same act with male lures although less frequently. Thus during instru-

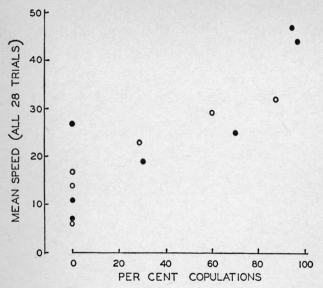

Fig. 2. Relation between strength of copulatory tendency (per cent attempts in total opportunities) and strength of the instrumental response. Filled circles indicate subjects who had female lures; open circles indicate subjects who had male "lures."

mental learning, copulators with female lures (Experimental Group) copulated in 73 per cent of their total opportunities, whereas copulators with male lures (Control Group) made the attempt in 44 per cent of the total opportunities. But if this difference is held constant, as in Fig. 2, by plotting instrumental performance as a function of amount of copulatory activity it would appear that *elicitation* of consummatory activity is the critical reinforcing factor rather than the sex of the lure or actual intromission.

DISCUSSION

The results demonstrate that performing the sex act innately reinforces instrumental behavior in rats regardless of whether consummation in the form of ejaculation is ever achieved. The males in this experiment had never ejaculated, either before or during the experiment, so the acquisition must be attributed to some aspect of the innately elicited copulatory activity and cannot be attributed to sex-drive reduction in any usual sense.[4]

The results do not clearly answer the question as to whether sexual *stimulation* was a critical factor in reinforcement of the instrumental response. In the comparison between the Experimental and Control Groups no noticeable difference is seen if frequency of copulation is held constant. That is, the female lures elicited more copulations but otherwise had no noticeable advantage over male lures as objects for mounting and making thrusts. Thus, as seen in Fig. 2, intromission and its presumably greater sexual stimulation did not add to reinforcement. On the surface this is contrary to a beneceptor theory of reinforcement (11), but unfortunately the findings are inconclusive because of the acquired reward factor. Thus the preliminary tests allowed intromission for all copulators, and the control group may have been reinforced by what might be called "conditioned beneception" if one interprets conditioning as an afferent modification process (3, 6). Further experimentation will be required to control the acquired reward factor permitted by the preliminary tests in the present study. It should be clear, however, that any acquired reward present was not based on drive reduction through ejaculation.

The results are in agreement with those of another study (8) in which sham feeding was achieved by using a solution of saccharine in water as reward for instrumental learning. Ingestion of a sweet solution without getting nourishment is comparable to copulating without achieving ejaculation. In each case the result was acquisition of the instrumental response, and in each case the same relation is found between the strength of the consummatory activity and the reinforcing power of the eliciting stimulus. That is, in the present study strength of instru-

[4] This assumes, of course, that normal males do not ejaculate in homosexual play, since these males lived in cages with other males. Beach and Holz (1) have noted homosexual ejaculation, but only for males made highly excitable by androgen treatment.

mental activity was a function of the frequency of copulation during limited exposure to the lure; in the saccharine study strength of instrumental activity was a function of rate of ingestion in a limited time. Thus in both studies the reinforcing power of the goal object was correlated with its prepotency in eliciting the appropriate consummatory response. While correlation and causation are not separated, both studies suggest that reinforcement is critically related to the ability of the goal object to elicit a dependable, prepotent response when presented. Of current theories this suggestion fits best the contiguity theory of Guthrie (4), which regards the ability of goal objects to take the animal out of the prior situation as the significant aspect of reinforcing events.

It may be argued that the present experiment cannot be treated as conclusive evidence against the drive-reduction interpretation since, if drive reduction is conceived in terms of reduction in overall stimulus intensity (7), it may be possible to demonstrate that each copulatory act relaxed a muscular tension innately initiated by the presence of goal object and the sex instinct. However, such an interpretation runs into complications if one considers the temporal relations involved in the succession of events: (1) instrumental act, (2) increase in tension through exposure to female, and (3) reduction in tension through mounting and making thrusts. It would appear that the "effect" following most closely after the learned response is an *increase* in tension even if each copulation were considered tension-reducing. On the whole the present findings emphasize the incentive value of rewards—rather than their satisfying or relaxing value—as a critical factor in selective learning.

SUMMARY

1. Using running and hurdle-climbing as the instrumental act, sexually naive male rats were rewarded by being given a female in heat or a male companion in the goal box. Sexual activity, but without ejaculation, was permitted during a brief confinement after reaching the goal box.

2. The results demonstrate that copulation without

ejaculation, and without any past history of ejaculation, functions as an effective reward for selective learning in male rats. Also, the strength of the instrumental response acquired was closely related to the strength of the copulatory tendency.

3. The results suggest that elicitation of a dependable and prepotent consummatory response is the critical factor in the reinforcement of instrumental responses rather than drive-reduction or beneception.

REFERENCES

1. Beach, F. A., and Holz, A. Marie. Mating behavior in male rats castrated at various ages and injected with androgen. *J. exp. Zool.*, 1946, 101, 91-142.
2. Beach, F. A., and Levinson, G. Diurnal variations in the mating behavior of male rats. *Proc. Soc. exp. Biol.*, *N. Y.*, 1949, 72, 78-80.
3. Birch, H. G., and Bitterman, M. E. Reinforcement and learning: The process of sensory integration. *Psychol. Rev.*, 1949, 56, 292-308.
4. Guthrie, E. R. The effect of outcome on learning. *Psychol. Rev.*, 1939, 46, 480-484.
5. Hull, C. L. *Principles of behavior*. New York: Appleton-Century, 1943.
6. Maier, N. R. F., and Schneirla, T. C. Mechanisms in conditioning. *Psychol. Rev.* 1942, 49, 117-134.
7. Miller, N. E., and Dollard, J. *Social learning and imitation*. New Haven, Conn.: Yale Univ. Press, 1941.
8. Sheffield, F. D., and Roby, T. B. Reward value of a nonnutritive sweet taste. *J., comp. physiol. Psychol.*, 1950, 43, 471-481.
9. Stone, C. P. The congenital sexual behavior of the young male albino rat. *J. comp. Psychol.*, 1922, 2, 95-153.
10. Stone, C. P., and Ferguson, L. W. Temporal relationships in the copulatory acts of adult male rats. *J. comp. Psychol.*, 1940, 30, 419-433.
11. Troland, L. T. *The fundamentals of human motivation*. New York: Van Nostrand, 1928.

17

Studies of Fear as an Acquirable Drive: I. Fear as Motivation and Fear-Reduction as Reinforcement in the Learning of New Responses[1]

NEAL E. MILLER
Yale University

The following selection demonstrates the acquirability of drives which, once acquired, can motivate the learning of new responses. Miller shows that painful experiences in a chamber will produce fear of that environment and that fear in the absence of pain can motivate the learning of new responses.

This selection is reprinted from the Journal of Experimental Psychology, 1948, 38, 89-101, *with the permission of the author and the American Psychological Association.*

An important role in human behavior is played by drives, such as fears, or desires for money, approval, or status, which appear to be learned during the socialization of the individual (1, 12, 16, 17, 18). While some studies have indicated that drives can be learned (2, 8, 15), the systematic experimental investigation of acquired drives has been scarcely begun. A great deal more work has been done on the innate, or primary drives such as hunger, thirst, and sex.

---

[1] This study is part of the research program of the Institute of Human Relations, Yale University. It was first reported as part of a paper at the 1941 meetings of the A.P.A. The author is indebted to Fred D. Sheffield for assistance in the exploratory work involved in establishing the experimental procedure and for criticizing the manuscript.

Fear is one of the most important of the acquirable drives because it can be acquired so readily and can become so strong. The great strength which fear can possess has been experimentally demonstrated in studies of conflict behavior. In one of these studies (3) it was found that albino rats, trained to run down an alley to secure food at a distinctive place and motivated by 46-hour hunger, would pull with a force of 50 gm. if they were restrained near the food. Other animals, that had learned to run away from the end of the same alley to escape electric shock, pulled with a force of 200 gm. when they were restrained near that place on trials during which they were not shocked and presumably were motivated only by fear. Furthermore, animals, that were first trained to run to the end of the alley to secure food and then given a moderately strong electric shock there, remained well away from the end of the alley, demonstrating that the habits motivated by fear were prepotent over those motivated by 46-hour hunger (9).[2] This experimental evidence is paralleled by many clinical observations which indicate that fear (or anxiety as it is called when its source is vague or obscured by repression) plays a leading role in the production of neurotic behavior (5, 6).

The purpose of the present experiment was to determine whether or not once fear is established as a new response to a given situation, it will exhibit the following functional properties characteristic of primary drives, such as hunger: (a) when present motivate so-called random behavior and (b) when suddenly reduced serve as a reinforcement to produce learning of the immediately preceding response.

APPARATUS AND PROCEDURE

The apparatus used in this experiment is illustrated in Fig. 1. It consisted of two compartments: one white with a grid as a floor and the other black with a smooth solid floor. Both of these had a glass front to enable the experimenter to observe the animal's behavior. The two compartments were separated by a door which was painted with horizontal black and white stripes. This door was held up by a catch operated by a solenoid and

---

[2] In both of these experiments the 46-hour food deprivation was made more effective by the fact that the animals had been habituated to a regular feeding schedule and maintained on a diet that was quantitatively restricted enough to keep them very thin but qualitatively enriched with brewer's yeast, cod liver oil, and greens to keep them healthy.

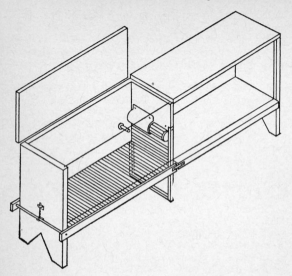

Fig. 1. Acquired drive apparatus. The left compartment is painted white, the right one black. A shock may be administered through the grid which is the floor of the white compartment. When the animal is placed on the grid which is pivoted at the inside end, it moves down slightly making a contact that starts an electric timer. When the animal performs the correct response, turning the wheel or pressing the bar as the case may be, he stops the clock and actuates a solenoid which allows the door, painted with horizontal black and white stripes, to drop. The E can also cause the door to drop by pressing a button. The dimensions of each compartment are 18 x 6 x 8½ in.

could be caused to drop in any one of three different ways: (a) by the E pushing a button, (b) by the rat moving a little cylindrical wheel made of horizontal rods stretched between bakelite disks and exposed above the right hand half of the door, (c) by a bar projecting 1¼ in. from the side of the apparatus in front of the upper left hand corner of the door.

The support of the grid was pivoted at the end near the door and held slightly above a contact by a little spring at the far end. Placing the rat into the apparatus caused the grid to move down a fraction of an inch and close the contact. This started an electric clock. When the animal caused the door to drop by rotating the wheel a fraction of a turn or pressing the bar (depending upon the way the apparatus was set), he stopped the clock which timed his response. The wheel was attached to a ratchet in such a way that the part of it facing the rat could only be moved downward. A brush riding on a segment of the wheel which projected through the back of the apparatus was arranged in such a way that each quarter of a revolution was recorded on an electric counter.

The animals used in this experiment were male albino rats approximately six months old. They had been tamed by handling but had not been used in any other experiment. They were allowed plenty of food and water in their home cages at all times.

The procedure involved the following five steps:

1. *Test for initial response to apparatus.*—The animals were placed in the apparatus for approximately one min. with the door between the two compartments open and their behavior was observed.

2. *Trials with primary drive of pain produced by electric shock.*—The procedure for administering shock was designed to attach the response of fear to as many as possible of the cues in the white compartment instead of merely to the relatively transient stimulus trace of just having been dropped in. This was done so that the animal would remain frightened when he was restrained in the compartment on subsequent non-shock trials. The strength of shock used was 500 volts of 60 cycle AC through a series resistance of 250,000 ohms. The animals were given 10 trials with shock. On the first trial they were allowed to remain in the white compartment for 60 sec. without shock and then given a momentary shock every five sec. for 60 sec. At the end of this period of time the E dropped the door and put a continuous shock on the grid.

As soon as the animal had run into the black compartment, the door was closed behind him and he was allowed to remain there for 30 sec. Then he was taken out and placed in a cage of wire mesh approximately nine in. in diameter and seven in. high for the time between trials. Since the animals were run in rotation in groups of three, the time between trials was that required to run the other two animals, but was never allowed to fall below 60 sec. This procedure was followed on all subsequent trials.

On the second trial the animal was placed into the center of the white compartment facing away from the door, was kept there for 30 sec. without shock, at the end of which time the shock was turned on and the door opened. On trials 3 through 10 the grid was electrified before the animal was dropped on it and the door was opened before he reached it. On odd numbered trials the animal was dropped at the end of the com-

partment away from the door and facing it; on even numbered
trials he was dropped in the center of the compartment facing
away from the door.

3. *Non-shock trials with experimenter dropping door.*—The
purpose of these trials was to determine whether or not the animals would continue to perform the original habit in the absence of the primary drive of pain from electric shock, and to
reduce their tendency to crouch in the white compartment and
to draw back in response to the sound and movement of the
door dropping in front of them.[3] Each animal was given five
of these non-shock trials during which the E dropped the door
before the animal reached it. As with the preceding trials the
animals were dropped in facing the door on odd numbered trials
and facing away from it on even numbered ones; they were
allowed to remain in the black compartment for 30 sec. and
were kept in the wire mesh cage for at least 60 sec. between
trials.

4. *Non-shock trials with door opened by turning the wheel.*
—The purpose of these trials was to determine whether the
continued running without shock was the mere automatic per-
sistence of a simple habit, or whether an acquired drive was
involved which could be used to motivate the learning of a new
habit. During these trials the E no longer dropped the door.

[3] During the training in the next step (learning to rotate the
wheel), crouching would interfere with the type of responses
necessary in order to hit the wheel and withdrawing would
prevent the animals from going into the black compartment
and having their fear reduced immediately after hitting the
wheel. Apparently crouching occupies a dominant position in
the innate hierarchy of responses to fear. Similarly withdrawing
seems to be either an innate or a previously learned response to
the pattern of fear plus a sudden stimulus in front of the
animal. During the shock trials the response of fear is learned
to the pattern of shock plus white compartment and the responses of running are learned to the pattern of shock plus
stimuli produced by the fear response plus the cues in the white
compartment. When the shock stimulus drops out of the pattern, the generalized fear and running responses elicited by
the remainder of the pattern are weaker. The innate crouching
response to fear is then in conflict with the generalized running
responses to the pattern of fear plus cues in the alley. If the
door is closed, the extinction of running and other related responses may reduce their strength to the point where crouching becomes dominant. If the door is dropped in front of the
animal so that he can immediately run out of the white compartment, the reduction in the strength of fear will be expected
to strengthen the relative dominance of running and related
responses to the stimulus of fear plus the cues in the white
compartment and the sight and sound of the door dropping.

The apparatus was set so that the only way the door could be dropped was by moving the wheel a small fraction of a turn. The bar was present but pressing it would not cause the door to drop. The animals that moved the wheel and caused the door to drop were allowed to remain 30 sec. in the black compartment. Those that did not move the wheel within 100 sec. were picked out of the white compartment at the end of that time. All animals remained at least 60 sec. between trials in the wire mesh cage. All animals were given 16 trials under these conditions. On each trial the time to move the wheel enough to drop the door was recorded on an electric clock and read to the nearest 10th of a sec.

5. *Non-shock trials with door opened by pressing the bar.*— The purpose of these trials was to determine whether or not animals (a) would unlearn the first new habit of turning the wheel if this habit was no longer effective in dropping the door, and (b) would learn a second new habit, pressing the bar, if this would cause the door to drop and allow them to remove themselves from the cues arousing the fear. Animals that had adopted the habit of crouching in the white compartment till the end of the 100 sec. limit and so had not learned to rotate the wheel were excluded from this part of the experiment. These trials were given in exactly the same way as the preceding ones except that the apparatus was set so that turning the wheel would not cause the door to drop but pressing the bar would. During these trials there was no time limit; the animals were allowed to remain in the white compartment until they finally pressed the bar.[4] The time to press the bar was recorded on an electric clock to the nearest 10th of a sec. and the number of revolutions of the wheel was recorded on an electric counter in quarter revolutions.

SUGGESTED IMPROVEMENTS IN PROCEDURE

In the light of further theoretical analysis and experimental results it is believed that the above procedure could be improved by the following changes: (a) Have the door drop down only part of the way so that it remains as a hurdle approximately two in. high over which the animals have to climb, thus introducing components of standing up and reaching into the initial response. This should favor the subsequent occurrence of wheel turning or bar pressing. (b) Connect the door to an elec-

[4] One animal which did not hit the bar within 30 min. was finally discarded.

tronic relay so that it will fall when touched and require the animals to touch it in order to make it fall during steps 2 and 3 of the experiment. This should tend to accomplish the same purpose as the preceding change and also insure that the animals have the response of running through the door attached to the stimulus produced by its dropping when they are very close to it. (c) Increase the number of non-shock trials in step 3 to approximately 12 in order to further counteract crouching. (d) At the end of the time limit in step 4, drop the door in front of the animal instead of lifting him out of the white compartment. This should tend to maintain the strength of the habit of going through the door and make it less likely that crouching or sitting will be learned.

RESULTS

In the test before the training with electric shock, the animals showed no readily discernible avoidance or preference for either of the two chambers of the apparatus. They explored freely through both of them.

During the trials with primary drive of pain produced by electric shock, all of the animals learned to run rapidly from the white compartment through the door, which was dropped in front of them by the E, and into the black compartment. On the five trials without shock, and with the E still dropping the door, the animals continued to run. The behavior of the animals was markedly different from what it had been before the training with the primary drive of pain from electric shock.

When the procedure of the non-shock trials was changed so that the E no longer dropped the door and it could only be opened by moving the wheel, the animals displayed variable behavior which tended to be concentrated in the region of the door. They would stand up in front of it, place their paws upon it, sniff around the edges, bite the bars of the grid they were standing on, run back and forth, etc. They also tended to crouch, urinate, and defecate. In the course of this behavior some of the animals performed responses, such as poking their noses between the bars of the wheel or placing their paws upon it, which caused it to move a fraction of a turn and actuate a contact that caused the door to open. Most of them then ran through into the black compartment almost immediately. A few of them drew back with an exaggerated startle response and crouched. Some of these eventually learned to go through the door; a few seemed to learn to avoid it. Other animals abandoned their trial-and-error behavior before they happened to strike the wheel and persisted in crouching so that they had to be lifted out of the white compartment at the end of the 100 sec. period. In general, the animals that had to be lifted out seemed to crouch sooner and sooner on successive trials.

Thirteen of the 25 animals moved the wheel enough to drop the door on four or more out of their first eight trials. Since, according to theory, a response has to occur before it can be reinforced and learned, the results of these animals were analyzed separately and they were the only ones which were subsequently used in the bar-pressing phase of the experiment.[5] The average speed (reciprocal of time in seconds) with which these animals opened the door by moving the wheel on the 16 successive trials is presented in Fig. 2. It can be seen that there is a definite tendency for the animals to learn to turn the wheel more rapidly on successive trials. Eleven out of the 13 individual animals turned the wheel sooner on the 16th than on the first trial, and the two animals which did not show improvement were ones which happened to turn the wheel fairly soon on the first trial and continued this performance throughout. The difference between the average speed on the first and 16th trials is of a magnitude $(t = 3.5)$ which would be expected to occur in the direction predicted by theory, less than two times in 1000 by chance. Therefore, it must be concluded that those animals that did turn the wheel and run out of the white compartment into the black one definitely learned to perform this new response more rapidly during the 16 trials

[5] In a subsequent experiment (13) in which further steps suggested by the theoretical analysis (see footnote 3 and SUGGESTED IMPROVEMENTS IN PROCEDURE) were taken to get rid of the crouching, none of the 24 animals in the group which had received the strong shock had to be eliminated for crouching; all of them learned to perform the new response during the non-shock trials.

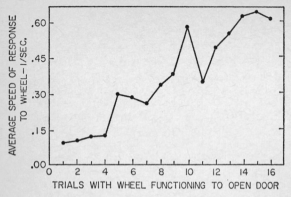

Fig. 2. Learning the first new habit, turning the wheel, during trials without primary drive. With mild pain produced by an electric shock as a primary drive, the animals have learned to run from the white compartment, through the open door, into the black compartment. Then they were given trials without any electric shock during which the door was closed but could be opened by turning a little wheel. Under these conditions the 13 out of the 25 animals which turned the wheel enough to drop the door on four or more of the first eight trials learned to turn it. This figure shows the progressive increase in the average speed with which these 13 animals ran up to the wheel and turned it enough to drop the door during the 16 non-shock trials.

without the primary drive of pain produced by electric shock.

When the setting on the apparatus was changed so that the wheel would not open the door but the bar would, the animals continued to respond to the wheel vigorously for some time. It was obvious that they had learned a strong habit of responding to it. Eventually, however, they stopped reacting to the wheel and began to perform other responses. After longer or shorter periods of variable behavior they finally hit the bar, caused the door to drop, and ran through rapidly into the black compartment. On the first trial the number of complete rotations of the wheel ranged from zero to 530 with a median of 4.75. On successive trials during which turn-

ing the wheel did not cause the door to drop, the amount
of activity on it progressively dropped till by the tenth
trial the range was from 0 to 0.25 rotations with a
median of zero. The progressive decrease in the amount
of activity on the wheel is shown in Fig. 3. It is plotted
in medians because of the skewed nature of the distribution. Twelve out of the 13 rats which were used in this
part of the experiment gave fewer rotations of the wheel
on the tenth than on the first trial. From the binomial
expansion it may be calculated that for 12 out of 13
cases to come out in the direction predicted by the theory
is an event which would be expected to occur by chance
less than one time in 1000. Thus, it may be concluded
that the dropping of the door, which is presumed to have
produced a reduction in the strength of fear by allowing

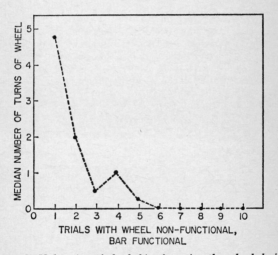

Fig. 3. *Unlearning of the habit of turning the wheel during
trials on which it no longer serves to reduce the acquired drive.
When conditions were changed so that turning the wheel was
ineffective (and pressing the bar was effective) in causing the
door to drop and allowing the animal to run from the white
into the black compartment, the animals showed a progressive
decrement in the response of rotating the wheel. Each point is
based on the median scores of 13 animals.*

the animals to excape from the cues in the white compartment which elicited the fear, was essential to the maintenance of the habit of rotating the wheel.

The results on bar pressing are presented in Fig. 4. It can be seen that the speed of bar pressing increased

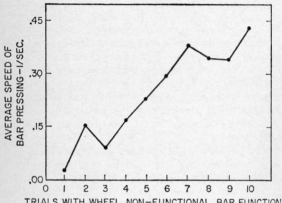

Fig. 4. *Learning a second new habit, bar pressing, under acquired drive. Conditions were changed so that only pressing the bar would cause the door to drop and allow the animals to run from the white compartment where they had been previously shocked, into the black one where they had escaped shock. During non-shock trials under these conditions, the animals learned a second new habit, pressing the bar. Each point is based on the average speed of 13 animals.*

throughout the 10 non-shock trials during which that response caused the door to drop. Since the last trial was faster than the first for 12 out of the 13 animals, the difference was again one which would be expected by chance less than one time in 1000.

DISCUSSION

On preliminary tests conducted before the training with electric shock was begun, the animals showed no noticeable tendency to avoid the white compartment.

During training with the primary drive of pain produced by electric shock in the white compartment, the animals learned a strong habit of quickly running out of it, through the open door, and into the black compartment.

On non-shock trials the animals persisted in running from the white compartment through the open door into the black one. On additional non-shock trials during which the door was not automatically dropped in front of the animals, they exhibited so-called random behavior and learned a new response, turning the wheel, which caused the door to drop and allowed them to escape into the black compartment. This trial-and-error learning of a new response demonstrated that the cues in the white compartment had acquired the functional properties of a drive and that escape from the white into the black compartment had acquired the functional properties of a reward.

At this point the results of two later experiments which serve as controls should be briefly mentioned. One of these (13) demonstrated that the capacity of the cues in the two compartments to motivate and reinforce new learning was a function of the strength of the primary drive involved in the previous stage of the training. Animals put through the same procedure in every respect except that the primary drive was a weak one produced by a 90 volt electric shock showed no tendency to learn a new habit (which in this case was bar pressing) on subsequent non-shock trials. Animals, given their initial training with a stronger primary drive produced by a 540 volt shock, showed rapid learning of the new response on subsequent non-shock trials. For these two groups all other features of the experiment were exactly the same including possible initial preferences for the different features of the two compartments and trials of running in the apparatus with the last response to the cues in the white compartment being going through the door into the black one, etc. Therefore, the difference in learning during the non-shock trials must have been a function of the previous training, and more specifically a function of the strength of the primary drive involved in that training.

The second experiment which serves as a control demonstrated that if the non-shock trials were continued long enough, the new habit of pressing the bar and the older response of running through the door would both eventually extinguish (11). Thus, in this situation the primary drive of pain is essential not only to the establishment of the acquired drive, but also to its maintenance.

In the present experiment, when the animals were dropped into the white compartment on the non-shock trials following their training with shock, they exhibited urination, defecation, tenseness, and other forms of behavior which are ordinarily considered to be symptoms of fear. Furthermore, the procedure of having been given a number of moderately painful shocks in this compartment would be expected to produce fear. Therefore, it seems reasonable to conclude that the acquirable drive motivating the learning of the new response of turning the wheel was fear and that a reduction in the strength of this fear was the reinforcing agent. Thus, this experiment confirms Mowrer's (14) hypothesis that fear (or anxiety) can play a role in learning similar to that of a primary drive such as hunger.

In terms of the hypothesis put forward in Miller and Dollard (12) the cues in the white compartment acquire their drive value by acquiring the capacity to elicit an internal response which produces a strong stimulus. Whether this strong stimulus is produced by peripheral responses, such as those involved in the blanching of the stomach and the tendency for hair to stand on end, or by central impulses which travel from the thalamus to sensory areas of the cortex is a matter of anatomical rather than functional significance. Fear may be called a stimulus-producing response if it shows the functional characteristics of such responses, in brief, obeys the laws of learning and serves as a cue to elicit learned responses such as the verbal report of fear.

The general pattern of the fear response and its capacity to produce a strong stimulus is determined by the innate structure of the animal. The connection between the pain and the fear is also presumably innate. But the connection between the cues in the white compartment and the fear was learned. Therefore the fear of the white compartment may be called an acquired drive. Because fear can be learned, it may be called acquirable; because it can motivate new learning, it may be called a drive.

Running through the door and into the black compartment removed the animal from the cues in the white compartment which were eliciting the fear and thus produced a reduction in the strength of the fear response and the stimuli which it produced. This reduction in the strength of the intense fear stimuli is presumably what gave the black compartment its acquired reinforcing value.

If the reduction in fear produced by running from the white into the black was the reinforcement for learning the new habit of wheel turning, we would expect this habit to show experimental extinction when that reinforcement was removed. This is exactly what happened. During the first trial on which turning the wheel no longer dropped the door, the animals gradually stopped performing this response and began to exhibit other responses. As would be expected, the one of these responses, pressing the bar, which caused the door to drop and allowed the animal to remove himself from the fear-producing cues in the white compartment, was gradually learned in a series of trials during which the wheel turning was progressively crowded out. Thus, it can be seen that the escape from the white compartment, which presumably produced a reduction in the strength of the fear, played a crucial role, similar to that of a primary reward, in the learning and maintenance of the new habits.

Some of the implications of the principles which this experiment has demonstrated should be mentioned briefly. It can be seen that being able to learn a response (fear of the white compartment) which in turn is able to motivate the learning and performance of a whole category of new responses (turning the wheel, pressing the bar, and any other means of escape from the white compartment) greatly increases the flexibility of learned behavior as a means of adapting to a changing environment.

The present experiment has demonstrated the drive

function of fear as a response which presumably produces a strong stimulus. But if fear is a strong response-produced stimulus, it will be expected to function, not only as a drive, but also as a cue mediating secondary generalization. Thus, when fear is learned as a new response to a given situation, all of the habits which have been learned elsewhere in response to fear, as well as the innate responses to fear, should tend to be transferred to that new situation. Evidence supporting this deduction has been secured in a recent experiment by May (7).

It seems possible that the potentialities of response-produced stimuli as mediators of secondary generalization and sources of acquirable drive may account in stimulus-response, law-of-effect terms for the type of behavior which has been described as 'expectancy' and considered to be an exception to this type of explanation. If it should turn out that all of the phenomena of expectancy can be explained on the basis of the drive and cue functions of response-produced stimuli, expectancy will of course not vanish; it will be established as a secondary principle derivable from more primary ones.

The mechanism of acquired drives allows behavior to be more adaptive in complex variable situations. It also allows behavior to appear more baffling and apparently lawless to any investigator who has not had the opportunity to observe the conditions under which the acquired drive was established. In the present experiment the learning and performance of the responses of turning the wheel and pressing the bar are readily understandable. An E dealing with many rats, a few of which without his knowledge had been shocked in the white compartment, might be puzzled by the fact that these few rats became so preoccupied with turning the wheel or pressing the bar. In the present experiment, the white and black compartments are very obvious features of the animal's environment. If more obscure external cues or internal ones had been involved, the habits of turning the wheel and pressing the bar might seem to be completely bizarre and maladaptive. One hypothesis is that neurotic symptoms, such as compulsions, are habits which are motivated by fear (or anxiety as it is called when its source is vague or obscured by repression) and reinforced by a reduction in fear.[6]

SUMMARY

Albino rats were placed in a simple apparatus consisting of two compartments separated by a door. One was white with a grid as a floor; the other was black without a grid. Before training, the animals showed no marked preference for either compartment. Then they were placed in the white compartment, received an electric shock from the grid, and escaped into the black compartment through the open door. After a number of such trials, the animals would run out of the white compartment even if no shock was on the grid.

To demonstrate that an acquired drive (fear or anxiety) had been established, the animals were taught a *new* habit *without further shocks.* The door (previously always open) was closed. The only way that the door could be opened was by rotating a little wheel, which was above the door, a fraction of a turn. Under these conditions, the animals exhibited trial-and-error behavior and gradually learned to escape from the white compartment by rotating the wheel.

If conditions were changed so that only pressing a bar would open the door, wheel turning extinguished, and a second new habit (bar pressing) was learned.

Control experiments demonstrated that the learning of the new habits was dependent upon having received moderately strong electric shocks during the first stages of training.

The following hypotheses were discussed: that responses which produce strong stimuli are the basis for acquired drives; that such responses may be the basis for certain of the phenomena of learning which have been labeled 'expectancy,' thus reducing this from the status of a primary to a secondary principle and that neurotic

---

[6] The author's views on this matter have been materially strengthened and sharpened by seeing the way in which Dollard (4), working with symptoms of war neuroses, has independently come to a similar hypothesis and been able to apply it convincingly to the concrete details of the case material.

symptoms, such as compulsions, may be motivated by anxiety and reinforced by anxiety-reduction like the two new responses learned in this experiment.

REFERENCES

1. ALLPORT, G. W. *Personality.* New York: Henry Holt, 1937.
2. ANDERSON, E. E. The externalization of drive: III. Maze learning by non-rewarded and by satiated rats. *J. genet. Psychol.,* 1941, 59, 397-426.
3. BROWN, J. S. Generalized approach and avoidance responses in relation to conflict behavior. New Haven: Dissertation, Yale Univ., 1940.
4. DOLLARD, J. Exploration of morale factors among combat air crewmen. *Memorandum to Experimental Section, Research Branch, Information and Education Division, War Department,* 9 March 1945.
5. FREUD, S. *New introductory lectures on psychoanalysis.* New York: Norton, 1933.
6. FREUD, S. *The problem of anxiety.* New York: Norton, 1936.
7. MAY, M. A. Experimentally acquired drives. *J. exp. Psychol.,* 1948, 38, 66-77.
8. MILLER, N. E. An experimental investigation of acquired drives. *Psychol. Bull.,* 1941, 38, 534-535.
9. MILLER, N. E. Experimental studies of conflict behavior. In: *Personality and the behavior disorders* (Ed. J. McV. Hunt), New York: Ronald Press, 1944, 431-465.
10. MILLER, N. E. Theory and experiment relating psychoanalytic displacement to stimulus-response generalization. *J. abnorm. soc. Psychol.* (In press)
11. MILLER, N. E. Studies of fear as an acquirable drive: II. Resistance to extinction. (In preparation)
12. MILLER, N. E., & DOLLARD, J. *Social learning and imitation.* New Haven: Yale Univ. Press, 1941.
13. MILLER, N. E., & LAWRENCE, D. H. Studies of fear as an acquirable drive: III. Effect of strength of electric shock as a primary drive and of number of trials with the primary drive on the strength of fear. (In preparation)
14. MOWRER, O. H. A stimulus-response analysis of anxiety and its role as a reinforcing agent. *Psychol. Rev.,* 1939, 46, 553-565.

15. MOWRER, O. H., & LAMOREAUX, R. R. Fear as an intervening variable in avoidance conditioning. *J. comp. Psychol.*, 1946, 39, 29-50.
16. SHAFFER, L. F. *The psychology of adjustment.* Boston: Houghton Mifflin, 1936.
17. WATSON, J. B. *Psychology from the standpoint of a behaviorist.* Philadelphia: Lippincott, 1924.
18. WOODWORTH, R. S. *Dynamic psychology.* New York: Columbia Univ. Press, 1918.

*Note

By the Editors of the Series

In the field of psychology we believe that the student ought to get the "feel" of experimentation by reading original source materials. In this way he can acquire a better understanding of the discipline by seeing scientific ideas grow and change. However, one of the main problems in teaching is the limited availability of these sources, which communicate most effectively the personality of the author and the excitement of ongoing research.

For these reasons we have decided to edit several books,* each devoted to a particular problem in psychology. In every case we attempt to select problems that have been and are controversial—that have been and still are alive. We intend to present these problems as a set of selected original articles, arranged in historical order and in order of progress in the field. We believe that it is important for the student to see that theories and researches build on what has gone before; that one study leads to another, that theory leads to research and then to revision of theory. We believe that *telling* the student this does not make the same kind of impression as letting him see it happen in actuality. The idea is for the student to read and build ideas for himself.

Suggestions for Use—These readings books can be used by the student in either of two ways. They are organized so that, with the help of the instructor (or of the students if used in seminars), a topic can be covered at length and in depth. This would necessitate lectures or discussions on articles not covered in the series to fill in the gaps. On the other hand, each book taken alone will give a student a good idea of the problem being covered and its historical background as well as its present state and the direction it seems to be taking.

---

* (Pub. note: a sub-series within the Insight Book Series.)